CHOCOLATE

The Tasty Treat
With a Dark Secret

CHOCOLATE

The Tasty Treat
With a Dark Secret

Margaret Briggs

Abbeydale Press

ISBN 978-1-86147-238-0

1 3 5 7 9 10 8 6 4 2

Published by Abbeydale Press
an imprint of Bookmart Ltd
Registered number 2372865
Trading as Bookmart Ltd
Blaby Road, Wigston, Leicester
LE18 4SE, England

Produced by Omnipress Limited, UK
Illustrations by Tegan Sharrard
Cover design by Omnipress Limited, UK

Printed in Dubai

ABOUT THE AUTHOR

Margaret Briggs was a teacher for 30 years, working in Kent, Germany, North Yorkshire and Sussex.

Since leaving teaching she has had more time for gardening and cooking and has embarked on a second career as a freelance writer, researcher and editor, alongside her writer husband, Lol. Six years ago the couple bought a dilapidated house in south-west France. The house is now restored and Margaret and Lol divide their time between Sussex and the Gironde, with two contrasting gardens to develop.

Margaret has written other books in this series: *Vinegar — 1001 Practical Uses, Gardening Hints and Tips, Porridge — Oats and their Many Uses, Honey — and its Many Health Benefits, Beetroot — The Vitality Plant & its Medicinal Benefits, Bicarbonate of Soda — A Very Versatile Natural Substance* and *Garlic & Onions — The Many Uses & Medicinal Benefits.*

CONTENTS

Introduction

Sit down, close your eyes and think of chocolate. Are you picturing a steaming mug of sweet, creamy chocolate or a bar of dark, smooth chocolate in a pristine foil wrap, with a satisfying snap as you break off the first piece? Is it an 86% cocoa solids, slightly bitter, thoroughly chocolate indulgence? Mmmm . . . sorry, I was miles away . . . or maybe it's a big chunk of milk chocolate that fills your entire mouth, or a flake. Oops, never mind the bits that have fallen off and are now scattered all over the sofa and your new top. You can deal with those later, when you've had your chocolate fix.

Maybe you chose a chocolate from a box. Milk or plain? Or maybe it was a chocolate bar filled with something sweet and yummy. So many choices, so much chocolate, so little time to try them all . . .

The first chocolate was served as a bitter drink by the indigenous peoples of Central America. Chilli, maize and other additions were to hand, but sugar didn't make its connection with chocolate for centuries and it took even longer for bars of milk chocolate to become the popular choice. We probably wouldn't even have recognised the drink as chocolate.

Chocolate as we know it is a relatively modern invention. Today the confectionery industry is big business, worldwide. We are told that chocolate, in moderation, is good for us as a healthy, energising food, with beneficial compounds ensuring continued health and happiness. Early consumers believed it was an aphrodisiac. Montezuma, the Aztec king, was certainly convinced by it.

This book gives a brief history of chocolate and explains the production of cocoa and chocolate. There are hints on how to enjoy it, as if you needed them. Most people stick with the chocolate they know and love, but trying a new variety could be a revelation: it may even change your life!

A Short
History of
Chocolate

PRE-COLOMBIAN TIMES

GOD FOOD
The cacao plant, from which cocoa powder is made, is said to have originated in the Amazon area of South America, 2000 BC. The earliest record of chocolate being consumed as a beverage dates from over 1,500 years ago in the rainforests of Central America, where conditions for the growth of the cacao tree were perfect. The Olmec, one of the first civilisations in the Americas, are believed to have been the first to grow cocoa beans as a domestic crop.

The Mayan word for the cacao tree was *cacahuaquchtl* and the word cacao means 'God food'. We get the word chocolate from the Mayan word *xocoatl*, meaning 'bitter water'.

EVIDENCE
The cacao tree was held in high esteem by the Mayan civilisation and by AD 300 cacao was used in ceremonies to celebrate life and fertility. Evidence of cacao pods has been found in the carvings remaining on temples and palaces. Later archaeological finds have included whole cacao beans and wood fragments from cacao trees in Guatemala. Vessels found to come from around 600–400 BC in Belize and 1100 BC in Honduras have been found, on scientific examination, to contain residue of theobromine and caffeine, which are both contained in cacao beans. Cacao is named in text on one of the vessels, which had a stirrup handle and a complicated, locking lid.

FLAVOURINGS
There are several mixtures of cacao described in ancient texts, for ceremonial and medicinal uses, as well as culinary purposes. It was used as a remedy and a way of delivering other herbal medicines. The cacao beans were roasted and pounded with chilli and maize for added flavour and then mixed with water. The bitter, unsweetened mixture was left to ferment and was originally reserved for ceremonies and for drinking by the rich, influential and religious elite. Women prepared the brew but, usually, only men drank it, as it was considered

too strong or possibly even toxic for women and children. Some mixtures included maize, chilli, vanilla, peanut butter and honey. Chocolate was also mixed with a variety of flowers, and sometimes it was thickened with corn gruel to make a kind of porridge. There were numerous variations, including a red variety made by adding annatto dye, or achiote.

HOT AND FROTHY
The Maya drank chocolate hot and frothy. It was produced by beating the cacao beans to a pulp on a grinding stone, as used for maize, then pouring the drink back and forth from a height or using a beater, called a molinillo. A vase has been found with an image of this froth-producing process.

MAYAN CIVILISATION
The Mayan civilisation spread across territory covering much of Central America and by AD 600 they had migrated to the south of Central America. Their empire reached from the Yucatán Peninsula of south-eastern Mexico down to Guatemala, Belize and western Honduras. In the Yucatán, the earliest known pods of cacao were cultivated in plantations, so that it was readily available for use in religious ceremonies. The basins of the Orinoco and Amazon rivers added further growing areas. Cacao was corrupted into the more familiar word cocoa by the European Conquistadors, of whom we shall hear more later on. The Maya believed that the cacao was discovered by the gods in a mountain that also contained other foods used by them. According to Mayan mythology, Hunahpú gave cacao to the Maya after humans were created from maize by the divine grandmother goddess, Ixmucané.

TRADING
Because cacao beans were valuable, they were given as gifts on occasions such as a child's coming of age and at religious ceremonies. The Mayan god Ek Chuah, the merchant god, was closely linked with cacao and the fruits were used at festivals in his honour. The Maya celebrated an annual festival in April to honour Ek Chuah. At this event the sacrifice of a dog with cacao-coloured markings was made, along with additional animal

sacrifices. Offerings of cacao, feathers and incense were made and there was an exchange of gifts.

Merchants often traded cacao beans for cloth, jade and ceremonial feathers. Farmers transported cacao beans to market by canoe or in large baskets strapped to their backs. If they were wealthy enough, merchants travelled further, employing porters.

There were no horses in Central America at the time, an important consideration in the later history of the continent. Some merchants ventured as far as Mexico, the land of the Aztecs, where they introduced them to the much-prized cacao beans and started a whole lot of trouble for the future.

TOLTECS

Around AD 950, a culture based in northern Mexico, at Tula, began to assert their influence in Central America, although their empire eventually declined. These people, known as the Toltecs, were a warlike people and expanded rapidly throughout Mexico, Guatemala and the Yucatán peninsula. Their society attained mythical proportions in the eyes of Central Americans long after their power faded, around 1200.

The Toltec people made the cacao tree a symbol of reincarnation of a tribal princess who had been murdered. The beans of the cacao were red and were, therefore, associated with blood and the bitter taste was said to represent the suffering she endured. Thus the suffering of the entire tribe was expressed through offerings of cacao. Toltec and Mayan cultures fused and the greatest centre was Chichén Itzá, on the very tip of the Yucatán peninsula. At one point the Toltecs were ruled by a man identified as a Topiltzin Quetzalcoatl.

AZTECS

The Aztecs also held cacao beans in high regard, but they lived further north than the Mayan people. Here conditions were not ideal for all-round production of cacao. The land was higher and more arid, so there had to be another way of acquiring the cacao. The Aztecs believed that Quetzalcoatl, a leader amongst other deities or gods, created cacao for the people. Quetzalcoatl is often called the feather serpent god and is the most well known Aztec god. His influence remained supreme for nearly 2,000 years across pre-Colombian civilisations. People believed that Quetzalcoatl was a god of vegetation and regeneration and that he taught men to grow cacao. An old Mexican Indian myth explains that Quetzalcoatl was forced to leave the country by a chief god, but was remembered by his devoted worshippers, who hoped he would return. Until this time, they had his legacy to sustain them — the cacao tree.

RITES AND RITUALS

Cacao was served as an offering at rites of passage ceremonies, from conception to birth and puberty, marriage, festivals and warfare. Some tribes anointed the bodies of young boys with flowers, water and powdered cacao. Cacao for other tribes was the link between the gods and earth, man and nature, and a source of fertility. It was also used in sacrifices to deities.

HEALTH BENEFITS

Both the Mayans and the Aztecs learned about the healthy effects of cocoa butter and made a balm to heal burns, ease sunburn and sores as well as treating liver problems and preventing snake bites. The Aztecs crushed the cacao beans on their knees, using a *metalt*, which was a mortar made from wood and iron that was lightly heated on a flat stone, called a *matate*. The beans were then roasted and crushed with spices, including pepper and cinnamon, before being sieved. Whilst the Maya liked hot chocolate, the Aztecs took their drink cold.

COUNTING BEANS

Cacao beans were valued so highly that, when dried, they were used as currency. Cacao beans were at the hub of a financial system that was accepted by the various tribes. Several important Central American civilisations began to develop trading based on a system other than bartering. Taxes and demands for money by invading Aztecs were so much easier in a unified system, with standard measures, introduced by the Maya. The standard measure of the

Maya was the *carga*, equivalent to the load that one man could carry on his back, fixed at 8,000 beans. The currency sheet was something like this:

1 zontle = 400 beans
20 zontles = 3 xiquipils
3 xiquipils or 8,000 beans = 1 carga
32 cargas = approximately 1 tonne

The 'tribute', or protection money, that groups had to pay their conquerors, in order to be freed from the yoke of slavery, was set in cargas. The annual taxation collected by the Aztec confederation was 980 cargas, or approximately 30 tonnes. A whole banking system grew up around the political structure. The buying power of good quality beans was impressive and counterfeiting of cacao beans was not unknown within the Aztec empire. In some areas, such as Yucatán, cacao beans were still used in place of small coins until the 1840s.

MISSED OPPORTUNITY
Christopher Columbus was the first European to come into contact with cacao. When Columbus returned triumphantly from America to the court of King Ferdinand and Queen Isabella of Spain, in 1492, he took many strange and impressive gifts. One which was overlooked was a collection of dark brown beans that were mistaken for almonds and failed to excite much interest.

Unfortunately, these were cocoa beans, but nobody knew what to do with them.

It took Columbus until his fourth voyage in 1502, to what is now Nicaragua, to discover cocoa beans used as currency, but he still didn't see the potential, intent as he was on discovering a route to India. He and his crew came across the largest dugout canoe they had ever seen. He wrote:

> '*A large local boat with 25 rowers came out to meet us. Their chief, sheltered by a roof, offered us cloth, beautiful copper objects and almonds which they use as money and from which they make a drink.*'

Colombus had his crew seize the vessel and its goods, and retained its skipper as his guide, but he still failed to appreciate the value of cacao. Columbus's son, Ferdinand, later remarked on how he was struck by the value the Native Americans placed on cacao beans, or almonds as he thought they were, saying:

> *'They seemed to hold these almonds at a great price; for when they were brought on board the ship together with their goods, I observed that when any of these almonds fell, they all stooped to pick it up, as if an eye had fallen.'*

BARGAINING POWER
At the beginning of the 16th century, Valdez, who travelled to America on an expedition in 1513, was offered a rabbit for 4 cacao beans, a prostitute for 10 and a slave for 100 beans.

MONTEZUMA II
By the time of the Spanish conquests, the Aztecs had created a powerful empire, and their armies conquered Mexico. Tributes in the form of food, cloth and luxury items, such as cacao beans, flowed into Tenochtitlan, founded in 1325, where the Aztec Emperor, Montezuma II, held court. The Aztecs were very superstitious people, with many gods. They believed that their world was constantly threatened by catastrophe. Great temples were built to honour Quetzalcoatl in Tenochtitlan, and Montezuma held him in particularly high esteem. Montezuma was born around 1480 and he reigned from 1502 until 1520. He is quoted as having said of cacao:

> *'The divine drink, which builds up resistance and fights fatigue. A cup of this precious drink permits a man to walk for a whole day without food.'*

Montezuma liked to drink his chocolate dyed red. He allegedly only drank it from a golden goblet, but is said to have drunk 50 cups a day, many of them before entering his harem. One story suggested that he threw the cups away each time, refusing to use them again, but surely even the rich and powerful Emperor of the Aztecs could not have been so careless. Much of his wealth, when discovered by the Spanish, was said to have been tied up in cacao beans.

In his *History of the Conquest of Mexico*, written in 1838, William Hickling relates how Aztec Emperor Montezuma

> 'took no other beverage than the chocolatl, a potation of chocolate, flavoured with vanilla and spices, and so prepared as to be reduced to a froth of the consistency of honey, which gradually dissolved in the mouth and was taken cold.'

Montezuma served chocolatl in a golden goblet to the conquistador Hernan Cortés.

DON CORTÉS

In 1519, Hernan Cortés arrived in April on the Tabasco coast. Some sources have suggested that the inhabitants, seeing him with his bearded white face and mounted on horseback and wearing armour, took him for the god Quetzalcoatl. A prophecy had told that this god had gone off to conquer new lands in the east and would return through his descendants. The conquistador was led to the flamboyant palace of the Emperor Montezuma where, as a sign of hospitality and in order to honour the god of cocoa growing, Cortés was offered a xocolatl, or chocolatl, in a golden goblet inset with tortoiseshell. Montezuma shared with Cortés his love of this thick beverage, sweetened with honey. He liked it for its aphrodisiac bitterness, accented with spices and chilli. Cortés tasted hot chocolate flavoured with cinnamon, pepper, cloves and achiote seeds, but seemed more impressed with the cup it was served in. In his first letter reporting back to Emperor Charles V, dated 1520, Cortés mentions chocolatl:

> 'which is a fruit like almonds that the natives sell in ground form. They value it so highly that it is treated like currency throughout their land and they buy with it everything they need, in the markets and elsewhere.'

At around the same time, the Spanish massacred the Aztec nobility and Cortés fled. Almost a year later, backed by tribes that opposed the Aztec domination and their practice of human sacrifice, he took Tenochtitlan and destroyed it. In 1522, he was appointed governor-general of New Spain. Cortés had the foresight to begin a plantation of cacao trees, not so much for the taste of the cocoa, as the powder produced was soon to be known, but for its conversion from beans to gold.

SPANISH CHOCOLATE MONOPOLY

At the time of the Spanish conquest, chocolate continued to have important ritual uses in native societies. Cacao beans had economic value as well, functioning economically as a unit of exchange. Major cacao-producing areas existed in coastal Tabasco and the Pacific coastal plain of colonial Guatemala and Chiapas.

In May 1520, the Spanish attacked a peaceful Aztec festival and killed Montezuma. Two months later the Aztecs had forced the Spanish out of the city of Tenochtitlan, but after regaining their strength, the Spanish and their allies held the city siege for 75 days, and its fall marked the end of the Aztec civilisation.

The Spaniards didn't appreciate chocolate at the beginning. Friar José de Acosta wrote:

> 'Loathsome to such as are not acquainted with it, having a scum or froth that is very unpleasant to taste. Yet it is a drink very much esteemed among the Indians, where with they feast noble men who pass through their country. The Spaniards, both men and women, that are accustomed to the country, are very greedy of this Chocolaté. They say they make diverse sorts of it, some hot, some cold, and some temperate, and put therein much of that 'chili'; yea, they make paste thereof, the which they say is good for the stomach and against the catarrh.'

Around 1528, Spanish ships headed for Spain with holds carrying sacks of cacao beans taken from Cortés's plantations. He presented these to King Charles V, along with the knowledge of how to prepare chocolatl. The drink was at first found to be bitter, but after numerous trials a recipe was created which replaced peppers with sugar, vanilla, nutmeg, cloves, allspice and cinnamon. This new recipe was found to be much more acceptable to the Spanish, who immediately created a state monopoly. The resulting demand from the Spanish nobility ensured a healthy income and a secret which was kept by the Spanish for almost a century. Chocolate enjoyed a reputation as an aphrodisiac because of the previous Aztec emperor's consumption, although the Aztecs considered chocolatl a healthy beverage rather than an aphrodisiac.

Cortés remained in Mexico until 1540 and began to appreciate the value of the cacao pods. In 1536, he estimated the price of cacao at around 5 to 6 gold pesos. Its price remained stable for a decade.

SECRET RECIPE
In 1544 Dominican friars took a delegation of Kekchi Mayan people to meet Prince Philip of Spain. They took gifts of cocoa in jars, ready to drink. Spanish monks kept the secret until 1580, before the news of a new sensation in beverages spread gradually across Europe and the first chocolate processing plant was set up in Spain. After Cortés's departure, the price of cocoa began to climb and reached 20 pesos per carga, the price set by an Act of 1551. Adopting the accounting and political system of the Aztecs, the Spanish imposed an annual tax. A system of cooperation, under the name '*encomienda*,' was established, to ensure that cultivation of the cacao plantations continued and provided a progressive harvest. Spain controlled all imports and colonists began to make money by cultivating cacao in other equatorial areas, such as Trinidad, Haiti, Mexico, Java and the Caribbean.

CHOCOLATE COINS
Beans were still used as currency in Mexico, where 100 beans was a daily wage for a porter and would buy a

turkey or a rabbit. Three beans would buy you a turkey egg or a fish to eat and one bean would buy a ripe avocado or a tomato.

WAKE UP AND SMELL THE COFFEE!
In 1579 English and Dutch buccaneers had a chance of uncovering the secret of chocolate, when they intercepted a Spanish 'treasure' ship, laden with cacao beans, returning from the New World. Unfortunately, the dashing pirates did not see the potential in their booty, and, thinking it was sheep dung, burned the lot of it!

A DROP IN THE OCEAN
A further chance came along in 1587, when another ship was captured, but, again, the cargo was considered useless and was destroyed. I suppose you don't miss what you've never had.

In 1585 the first cargo-load of cacao from Vera Cruz was unloaded in Seville. There wasn't a lot of interest expressed, apart from that of botanists. Cacao beans were in short supply and the special chocolate drink recipe was a closely guarded secret, but you had to know what you were buying, as well as what to do with it.

CHOCOLATE FAST . . .
As the Spanish settled and mixed with the Native Indian populations, chocolate took on an increasingly important role, as Spaniards overcame their aversion to it by mixing in vanilla, cinnamon and sugar. Christianity, in the form of the Catholic Church, brought new conflicts. Pope Pius V did not like the new chocolate drink, but obviously saw the way the wind was blowing, as, in 1569, he declared that drinking chocolate on a Friday was acceptable and did not constitute a breaking of the fast, as it was a drink

. . . AND LOOSE
 Because of its dark colour and grainy texture, chocolate provided an ideal cover for items associated with sexual witchcraft. These included various powders and herbs, as well as female body fluids, which women then mixed into a drink and fed to men to try to control their sexuality.

SOCIETY AND CHOCOLATE

By the 17th century, the consumption of chocolate had become well established in the new colonies of Central America. Guatemalans from all social and ethnic groups had access to chocolate, in cities such as Santiago, and they drank it in a wide range of contexts in daily life. The cultural meanings of chocolate had developed from ancient Mayan ritual and had been transformed, often leading to associations with female social disorder and witchcraft.

WOMEN'S WORK

Native women working as servants in colonial kitchens prepared the beverage and some men and women consumed large quantities of chocolate beverages daily, especially at breakfast. Mourners drank chocolate to fortify themselves during all-night wakes as well as for fiestas and other events. Female market sellers also sold chocolate drinks on stalls in the capital's outdoor markets. Only in extreme cases did men prepare chocolate, as you will discover below.

THE SPANISH INQUISITION

The Inquisition, which stretched as far as the new colonies, contained records of numerous alleged incidents, where, for instance, a woman reportedly served bewitched chocolate drinks to her slaves to prevent them from interfering in her sorcery and to keep them from running away.

One case brought to the Inquisition authorities asserted that a man's wife had bewitched him with sorcery. The husband, Juan, charged that Cecilia, his wife, had used spells and curses which reversed their gender roles and messed with his virility. He got up early and made the chocolate, while his wife stayed in bed. This 'unnatural behaviour', he said, was brought on by his wife's sorcery. The Inquisition gave the following summary of his testimony:

> *'His wife treats him not as a husband but as a servant. He lights the fire in the kitchen, he boils the water, he mixes the chocolate and heats the food . . . and he gets up very early every morning to do this while his wife*

stays in bed and sleeps until very late. And when his wife wakes, he brings her chocolate so she can drink it after she dresses. And even though it is very late [in the morning], he has the water ready, [and] he drinks chocolate with his wife . . . in this way his wife has turned him into a coward, and all this cannot be a natural thing.'

Cecilia was, of course, found guilty of witchcraft and banished. I'm so glad to think that I'm countering the usual, stereotypical roles in our house; I'm obviously doing the right thing, by making the early morning tea nine times out of ten! Good job it's not coffee!

CHOCOLATE IN CHURCH
Thomas Gage, an Englishman travelling in Central America in the 17th century, published a book in 1648, entitled *The English-American: His Travail by Sea and Land; or, a New Survey of the West-Indies*. He related how the role of chocolate acted as a vehicle of women's ritual power, and recalled how chocolate was used as the basis for magical potions, to cast supernatural illness, in sexual witchcraft practices, and to create disorderly behaviour in public settings, including churches.

Gage also described a public confrontation between the Bishop of Chiapas and his elite female parishioners over the consumption of hot chocolate during mass.

STORM IN A CHOCOLATE CUP
In San Cristobal de las Casa, in Chiapas, upper class Spaniards were consuming more and more chocolate. Some women were so addicted to chocolate that they had a finely carved goblet of it served to them every two hours. With the coming of Christianity, long religious services were not allowed to interfere with this ritual.

Bishop Bernardino de Salazar complained that this behaviour by the women was disrupting the mass. The bishop declared that he would excommunicate those women who continued to drink chocolate in church. The women unsuccessfully tried to change the bishop's mind, and Gage wrote:

> '*The women, seeing [the bishop] so hard to be
> entreated, began to stomacke him the more and to
> sleight him with scornfull and reproachfull words; others
> sleighted his excommunication, drinking in iniquity in
> the Church, as the fish doth water, which caused one
> day such an uproar in the Cathedrall, that many swords
> were drawne against the Priests and Prebends, who
> attempted to take away from the maids the cups of
> chocolatte, which they brought unto their mistresses.*'

Swords were drawn to protect chocolate, in church. Just
imagine the headlines today! The conflict escalated, with
both sides refusing to compromise and: 'The women
would not obey.'

Some of the congregation began to boycott services,
attending convents to worship instead, where nuns made
a pretty good cup of chocolate. When the bishop became
ill during the boycott, rumours spread throughout the
city, that one of the women had poisoned his chocolate.
The bishop's head and face became greatly swollen, and
any touch 'caused his skin to break and cast out white
matter, which had corrupted and overflowne all his body.'

Physicians called to attend the bishop agreed that
someone had poisoned him, and he died from his illness a
week later.

HEALING POWERS
Fortunately, chocolate had properties associated with
healing as well. Hospitals in Santiago budgeted for
chocolate among food expenditure for their patients.
In addition, chocolate was purchased for the priests
who cared for the sick and for hospital servants.

FIRST BRAZILIAN PLANTATION
Brazil first established cocoa plantations in the State of
Par, in 1677. This was the start of a very important export
business in centuries to come. By 1810 Venezuela was
producing half of the world's cocoa, a third of which was
drunk by Spaniards.

17TH-CENTURY DEVELOPMENTS IN EUROPE

At the beginning of the 17th century, Spain controlled the import of all cacao beans. They also began to cultivate cacao in other areas near the equator such as Trinidad, Haiti, Mexico, Java and the Caribbean, while carefully protecting their business.

In the 17th century, Dutch navigators helped to break Spain's monopoly of cocoa when they captured Curacao. They took cacao beans from America to Holland, where cocoa was highly prized and recommended by doctors as a cure for almost every ailment. Knowledge spread across Europe, and other powerful countries with empires of their own, such as France and Britain, became interested in cultivating cacao and producing chocolate in the Cameroons, Malaysia and West Africa. In the 1670s, a seafarer called Pedro Bravos do los Camerinos decided that he had had enough of exploration and settled in the Philippines, where he introduced cacao as a domestic crop. Cacao has been produced there ever since.

CHOCOLATE BOOK
By 1606 chocolate had become popular in Italy. An Italian traveller and explorer of world markets, Francesco d'Antonio Carletti, visited Central America and saw how the local people prepared cacao beans for a drink. He wrote down his findings and took the ideas back to Italy, eventually breaking the Spanish monopoly, although it took a long while for his manuscript to be published, early in the 18th century. In 1609, a book devoted entirely to chocolate was written in Mexico, although the author remains anonymous.

CHOCOLATE ARRIVES IN FRANCE
The secret of chocolate was taken to France in 1615, when Anne of Austria, the daughter of Philip II of Spain, married King Louis XIII of France. The French aristocracy enjoyed this new exotic drink. In 1643, when Princess

Maria Theresa of Spain was engaged to Louis XIV, she gave her five-year-old fiancé a gift of chocolate in an ornate chest. They did not marry until 1660, but Maria Theresa was said to have had one servant whose sole function was to prepare her favourite chocolate drink.

In 1659 Louis XIV granted David Chaillou the exclusive right to the *'making, selling and retailing in the entire kingdom an unusual composition called chocolate'* in his shop in Paris, which he continued to do for the next 15 or so years. This shop provided the focus for high society's growing adoration of chocolate. It became high fashion to consume this exotic beverage, even though enjoyment of chocolate was restricted to the French aristocracy.

Louis XIV started the cultivation of cacao trees in some of his colonies. In 1693, he created the corporation of the *limonadiers* (they didn't just sell lemonade), who were limited in number to 150 and were authorised to sell the chocolate beverage.

Chocolate reached Germany in about 1646, when it was brought back by visitors to Italy. The secret of the aromatic chocolate-flavoured drinks reached England from France soon after and they became very popular at the court of King Charles II.

In 1657 the first chocolate house was opened in London, by a Frenchman. High import duties kept the drink at a high price. It advertised

> *'In Bishopgate Street, in Queen's Head Alley, at a Frenchman's house, is an excellent West Indian drink called Chocolate to be sold, where you may have it ready at any time and also unmade at reasonable rates.'*

Tea and coffee arrived at about the same time in England and they soon became much cheaper than chocolate, which was kept for the elite. Within a decade, Samuel Pepys began to make regular mention of drinking chocolate in his diaries. Having spent the day and night celebrating the crowning of Charles II, he headed to his favourite chocolate house where the owner

'Did give me a chocolate to settle my stomach.'

Other fashionable chocolate houses soon opened, where people who could afford it would meet their friends to enjoy various rich chocolate drinks. Many of these were rather bitter to taste. One famous London chocolate drinking establishment was called White's Chocolate House, in St James Street. It was opened in 1693 by Frances White, an Italian immigrant. The chocolate drinks were served along with ale, beer and coffee. Chocolate beverages would have been made from blocks of solid cocoa, probably imported from Spain. Also on sale was a pressed cake of cocoa, which could be taken home to make the drink. At the end of the 17th century the first porcelain chocolate cup was produced. The earliest known chocolate pot in Britain dates from 1685. It was made in silver by George Garthorne.

CHOCOLATE IN ITALY, CIRCA 1660
The influential scientist Francesco Redi was a physician and author. As well as proving that rotting meat did not spontaneously generate maggots unless flies deposited eggs in it, he also devised many luxurious recipes for drinking chocolate. Among these were concoctions perfumed with ambergris and musk, as well as a recipe for jasmine-scented chocolate. In case you were wondering, ambergris is a solid waxy substance, secreted from the intestines of sperm whales, and is found floating in the sea or on sandy beaches. It was used to fix perfumes before a synthetic product was made. Lovely!

SLOANE RANGER
Sir Hans Sloane was born in County Down, Ireland, in 1660. He had a love of natural history and studied medicine. He is remembered for two reasons by the naming of Sloane Square in London: firstly, by bequeathing his collection of items to the nation, in what became the Natural History Museum, and secondly, for 'inventing' milk chocolate. Having travelled through France he became a fellow of the College of Physicians before travelling to Jamaica near the end of the century. During a stay of just over a year, he noted over 800 new species of plants and experienced cocoa as a drink. He

apparently found it nauseating, made with water, but when mixed with milk, he found it quite palatable. He took the recipe back to England, where it later became the original Cadbury Milk recipe. It was sold by apothecaries as a medicine until Sloane's drinking chocolate was manufactured by the chocolate giants in the 19th century.

THE COFFEE MILL AND THE TOBACCO ROLL
This was the name of a chocolate house, opened in 1674, specialising in neither of the substances suggested by its name. The chocolate house was famous for selling chocolate in cakes and in rolls, as the Spaniards ate it.

SUN KING
Chocolate became very popular during King Louis XIV of France's 72-year reign. Louis XIV had the foresight to engage a manufacturer to produce and sell chocolate on an economic scale. Louis was known as the Sun King and during his long life he was said to have enjoyed the erotic pleasures aroused by chocolate. He certainly seems to have had a lot of love interest, in terms of two wives and many affairs. In 1662, after consulting with his Jesuit advisers, he declared that the drinking of chocolate did not break the fast before Easter. Pope Gregory XIII confirmed this. The supply of cacao beans to the French market increased greatly after 1684, when France conquered Cuba and Haiti and set up their own cacao plantations. Madame de Maintenon, Louis's rather puritanical, second wife, persuaded him to ease off consumption at Versailles by 1693, but apparently he was still making love twice a day, at the age of 72!

CHOCOLATE BREAK-FAST
Spiritual matters and chocolate consumption reared their heads again in 17th-century Europe, when religious leaders found themselves engaged in arguments about whether chocolate was a beverage or a food. As we saw earlier, religious fasts which denied the taking of nourishment, didn't include chocolate because it was a drink. Those who were fasting took chocolate because it was nourishing and eased their hunger. Most people, including all of the popes from Gregory XIII to Benedict

XIV, agreed that it did not break the fast. Nevertheless, many took a more puritanical view, including, possibly, Madame de Maintenon, who converted from Protestantism to Catholicism, maintaining that it was far too nourishing and sustaining to be permissible.

18TH-CENTURY CHOCOLATE

TAXES AND TRANSFER LISTS
The English habit of improving the drink by adding milk caught on. By the end of the 18th century, London's chocolate houses began to disappear or change into more fashionable gentlemen's clubs. Hot chocolate was available, but still at a price, until the import tax was eliminated in 1853. At the beginning of the 18th century, Frederick I of Prussia decided to tax chocolate as an import in Germany.

In 1711, Emperor Charles VI transferred his court from Madrid to Vienna and chocolate moved to Vienna with the court. Soon after, Italian chocolatiers began serving chocolate in Florence and Venice and it wasn't long before they were welcomed in Switzerland, Germany and France.

LOVE POTIONS
Chocolate's reputation as an aphrodisiac continued to flourish in France. When Louis XV came to the throne in 1723 chocolate had become an institution in France. Madame de Pompadour, mistress to Louis XV, was told to try using chocolate with ambergris, in her quest to improve her libido. It obviously didn't work, although they remained friends for 15 years. Madame du Barry, however, encouraged her lovers to keep drinking chocolate, so that they could keep up with her insatiable demands.

THEOBROMA
In 1753, Swedish naturalist and biologist Carolus Linnaeus established a binomial system for classifying living organisms. The cacao tree's botanical name was given as *Theobroma*, which is Greek for 'Food of the Gods'.

TECHNOLOGY TAKES OVER

Soon technological breakthroughs started to make improvements in the supply of chocolate. In 1732, the design of a French inventor called Dubuisson allowed workers to stand and grind cacao beans at a 'table' which was heated from underneath by charcoal. This form of barbecue made production easier, apparently. I can't think that it was very comfortable, though. A modified steam engine soon mechanised the grinding process and the price of cocoa started to come down.

CHOCOLATE IN AMERICA

In 1755 chocolate finally reached North America, where production quickly became big business. Chocolate became accepted by the American colonists of New England, after fishermen from Gloucester, Massachusetts, accepted cacao beans as payment for cargo in Central America. Dr James Baker of Massachusetts and John Hannon from Ireland joined up for one of the earliest machine-based chocolate manufacturing enterprises, in 1765. They used an old grist mill to grind cacao beans into chocolate liquor. This was pressed into pastels for making into drinking chocolate. Their company, originally known as Hannon's Best Chocolate, was renamed after Hannon was lost at sea while on a cocoa-buying voyage to the West Indies. It was rebranded as the Baker Company and remained in the family until 1927. More chocolate history from North America follows, in a later section.

The first chocolate factory in Spain opened in Barcelona in 1780. In 1792 a factory opened in Berlin, run by brothers from Grisons in the Swiss Alps. Following James Watt's invention of the steam engine, in 1765, the technology was, fairly rapidly, applied to chocolate manufacture. J S Fry and Sons first used steam power in England in 1795. You can read more about this family later on.

POISONOUS CHOCOLATE

The Marquis de Sade, who was born in 1740 and died in 1814, was a passionate gourmet and a pretty nasty piece of work. He loved delicacies, such as quail stuffed with grape leaves, very fresh cream of chard soups and chocolate cake. He once wrote to his wife, from jail:

> *'I wish for a chocolate cake so dense, that it is black, like the devil's ass is blackened by smoke.'*

He used chocolate as a way of poisoning his victims and collaborators, as apparently at a ball in Marseille, where he served chocolate drops laced with aphrodisiacs and Spanish flies, to induce irritation. Large amounts of drugs seem to have been involved as well. He also described in his novels, some written in prison, poisons delivered in sweet chocolate concoctions.

DEATH BY CHOCOLATE

Although unsubstantiated, rumours surrounding the death of Pope Clement XIV, in 1774, hinted that chocolate was, as had been seen in Central America with the unfortunate Bishop of Chiapas, considered a particularly good medium for administering poison to priests. The Pope, whose usual constitution was quite vigorous, fell into a sickness, generally attributed to poison, although no conclusive evidence was ever produced. Claims of poisoning were denied by those closest to him. He was believed to have been killed with a cup of poisoned chocolate by Jesuits, whom he had suppressed the year before he died. The confectioner who served him and shared the beverage also died. It was said that the embalmer's arms swelled after touching the body.

CHOCOLATE POT

During the late 17th century, the chocolatière was invented. This provided a special tall pot for serving the beverage, so that it could be served frothy. The lid had a hole in the top, through which a molinillo, as used by the Maya people, was fitted.

GIACOMO CASANOVA

Casanova-(1725–98), the world's most famous lover, believed that chocolate was an aphrodisiac. He is said to have drunk chocolate before making love, savouring it before every romantic escapade, so his lifetime consumption of the beverage must have been huge! He probably didn't know that eating it helped his health, although it may well have provided the energy he needed to sustain his stamina. Casanova apparently used champagne as well as chocolate, a winning combination in my book.

DESPERATE DESPINA

In 1790, Mozart immortalised chocolate in his opera *Cosi fan Tutte*. At the time, hot chocolate was a drink only for the aristocracy. In his opera, Despina, the maid, is incensed by the fact that she has never tasted the hot chocolate she painstakingly prepares for her ladies. She stages a silent protest and decides to take a drink at last, but is found out.

MARIE ANTOINETTE

The last queen of France, Marie Antoinette, had a personal chocolatier from Vienna. She apparently had a poor appetite, so such delicacies as chocolate mixed with powdered orchid bulbs to plump out her figure, orange blossoms to soothe frayed nerves, and milk made of almonds to support a delicate stomach, were created. A much maligned and, I think, misreported queen, she was guillotined in 1793.

19TH-AND 20TH-CENTURY CHOCOLATE

It wasn't until the 19th century that chocolate took off as anything other than a drink. The preparation up until then was still pretty time-consuming and cocoa processing was carried out on a fairly small scale.

GOING DUTCH

In 1828, Dutch cocoa was invented by a chemist called Conraad Van Houten. He was a chocolate manufacturer in Amsterdam and he patented an invention that was soon to revolutionise chocolate: from a beverage to a confection. He devised a process for making chocolate powder by using hydraulic pressure. This removed almost half of the cocoa butter from chocolate liquor and reduced the fat content from over 50% to about 25%. It made a hard cake that could be pulverised to a powder and treated with alkaline salts, which made it easier to mix the powder with warm water. It also made the colour darker and also gave a smoother consistency. The removal of some of the bitterness made for more popular taste. This treatment came to be known as Dutching.

CHOCOLATE IN BRITAIN
During Victorian times, chocolate in Britain was dominated by three Quaker family businesses, with several common values. In 1824, at the age of 23, Quaker John Cadbury was given a sum of money by his father and allegedly told to 'sink or swim'. Cadbury opened a shop selling tea, coffee and cocoa. As part of the business, he roasted and ground his own cacao beans. Soon, he decided to concentrate on manufacturing chocolate. Perhaps the popularity of cocoa spread because of curious people peering in through the window. The shop became known for its plate glass window, the first in Birmingham, as well as for employing a Chinese clerk at the tea counter.

Founded in 1864, the Rowntree confectionery factory in York later became famous for a number of chocolate products, as well as for its advanced policies of industrial welfare.

There is a lot more information on both of these families later on.

THE FIRST CHOCOLATE BAR
The chocolate manufacturer, Joseph Fry and Son was founded by a Quaker who had been a doctor before opening the business. His son, also named Joseph Fry, bought a Watts steam engine to grind the cacao. In 1847, the family firm discovered a way to mix some of the melted cacao butter with sugar, back into defatted, or Dutched, cocoa powder. This created a paste that could be pressed into a mould to make a bar. Finally chocolate could be eaten as well as drunk.

TERRY'S OF YORK
York had another great British chocolate name in Terry's, the firm that began in 1767. It was founded by Mr Bayldon and Mr Berry. The Terry's name first appeared when Joseph Terry became a partner in 1823. The site remained the hub of Terry's confectionery production in Britain, at peak seasons employing over 700 people in the production of, amongst other things, their famous plain chocolate assortment. The York factory closed in the summer of 2005, moving its operation to mainland Europe.

THE GREAT EXHIBITION
In 1851 Queen Victoria's husband, Prince Albert, orchestrated the Great Exhibition in London. It was the first time citizens of the United States were introduced to bonbons, chocolate creams, boiled sweets and caramels.

AFFORDABLE CHOCOLATE
As part of his policy for promoting economic prosperity in England, William Gladstone reduced the taxes on cacao beans in 1853. This made cocoa much more attractive to British manufacturers.

IMPROVED STANDARDS
As a result of investigations by the British journal, the *Lancet*, it was discovered that significant food adulteration was practised by manufacturers, including the adding of brick dust to chocolate powder. In 1860, the first British Food and Drugs Act was passed.

BY APPOINTMENT
In 1854, Cadbury had received a Royal Warrant to be the sole purveyor of cocoa and chocolate to Queen Victoria. In 1866, Richard and George Cadbury purchased a Van Houtten machine for the factory and began to market their own cocoa powder. As another achievement and mark of distinction, the Cadbury family started the trend of mass produced, boxed chocolates in 1868, although a heart-shaped chocolate box for Valentine's Day was made in 1861. The first boxes of chocolates were packed and decorated in the sentimental, Victorian style of the day.

HAPPY NEW YEAR

During the Boer War, soldiers received a special 1900 New Year gift from Queen Victoria, in the form of chocolate bars.

ABSOLUTELY PURE: THEREFORE BEST

Since the invention of the Dutching method, people had been extracting cocoa butter from chocolate in order to make powdered cocoa, but had to use additives to keep the chocolate powdery. In 1866, the Cadbury family were able to eliminate additives by discovering an improved method of extracting the natural cocoa butter. This innovation allowed the firm to advertise their product as 'Absolutely Pure: Therefore Best' and at the same time provided extra cocoa butter for sweet-making.

MILK CHOCOLATE

Milk chocolate came a little later, and the Quaker producers did not invent it. That was done by Daniel Peters, in Switzerland. They did, however, become leaders in making and selling milk chocolate. Cadbury's introduced milk chocolate in 1897, and Fry's in 1902. Early milk chocolate bars were not particularly good and Cadbury's spent years developing a superior milk chocolate, with new production processes. This effort paid off with the introduction of Cadbury's Dairy Milk in 1905. By 1913, it was the company's best seller. Today, it is popular worldwide.

CHOCOLATE AND
THE RELIGIOUS SOCIETY OF FRIENDS

The Religious Society of Friends, commonly known as Quakers, was founded in England in the 17th century. A pacifist, Christian denomination, the Quakers evolved from Puritans before the English Civil War, and were dissatisfied with the existing denominations and sects of Christianity. Since they were not members of the Church of England, they were denied the opportunity of university education and the right to hold public office until the 19th century. The medical profession, however, was open to Friends, since in those days it was learned primarily by apprenticeship and not through university education. This was significant for Friends' involvement with chocolate, since in the 17th and early 18th centuries chocolate was recommended by physicians for its medicinal qualities.

Beliefs prohibited many normal business activities and many Quakers involved themselves in retail trade and manufacturing. Baking was a common occupation because of the association of bread as the 'staff of life'. Bakers in England were the first to add chocolate to cakes during the 1600s, so there was a natural progression for them to start making pure chocolate. Three cities in England that became associated with chocolate-making were also cities with communities of Friends. These were Bristol, Birmingham and York.

BRISTOL
In 1748, a physician named Joseph Fry had opened an apothecary shop in Bristol. He taught himself a number of recipes for chocolate and, in 1761, he purchased the Churchman apothecary shop. His son, Joseph Storrs Fry, patented a new technique for grinding cacao beans in 1795, using the Watts steam engine, and was the first chocolate manufacturer to introduce factory methods to the industry.

BIRMINGHAM
In 1824, John Cadbury opened up a small shop in Birmingham, selling cocoa among other things. In 1831, he rented a small factory to make chocolate and cocoa for drinking. The enterprise prospered and he took his brother Benjamin into the business in 1847. They rented a larger factory and the business never looked back.

YORK
In York, the Rowntree family were in the chocolate business. Joseph Rowntree, the son of a Quaker grocer, was born in York in 1834. After only five years of schooling Joseph began work as a grocer, with his father. While learning the business, in London, he developed a lifelong interest in politics and regularly attended debates at the House of Commons. In 1869 he left to join

his brother, Henry Rowntree, who owned the Cocoa, Chocolate and Chicory Works in York.

FRIENDS AND PHILANTHROPISTS
From their earliest beginnings in business, the Religious Society of Friends were noted for their enlightened treatment of their employees, providing everything needed for workers to better themselves, such as good housing, welfare and education. George Cadbury was active in the Garden City movement. When the company needed to build a new factory, the Cadbury family decided to move out of unhealthy, polluted Birmingham to a country location on the outskirts of the city. George Cadbury built a village for employees, called Bournville. John Cadbury was an active member of the Temperance movement. He felt that alcohol was a major cause of poverty and illness amongst working people. The Friends therefore saw chocolate as a healthy alternative to alcohol, and wished to make it available to working people, at a time when chocolate could only be afforded by the richer classes.

ENLIGHTENED IDEAS
When the new Bournville factory was built in 1879, there were also 16 houses constructed for senior employees. Conditions and benefits were superior to those workers generally knew in the Victorian era. The factory had heated dressing rooms, kitchens, gardens, and extensive sports fields. Special workers' fares were agreed with the railway company and swimming pools were even provided. In 1866, workers were encouraged in their spiritual development by morning prayers and Bible readings, practices which continued for half a century.

GARDEN CITIES
In 1895, George bought an additional 120 acres and began to build more houses in the garden city. There were also libraries, churches and shops in the village. His goal was to provide affordable housing for wage earners in a healthy environment. Unlike some other communities built by philanthropic factory owners at the time, where religious observance and strict laws on activities were imposed on workers, the community was not just limited

to Cadbury workers, and was designed to be mixed in both class and occupation. Groups of cottages were set back from tree-lined roads and each plot had space for a garden. Building was restricted so that gardens were not overshadowed. What is more, George Cadbury founded the Bournville Village Trust in 1900, to preserve the village for generations to come. The Trust continues to follow the original principles, including the preservation of parks and open spaces and diversification of the population.

WELFARE AND LABOUR RELATIONS

The Cadbury family were pioneers in employee welfare and labour relations. Cadbury Brothers was the first firm to introduce the Saturday half-day holiday, and also pioneered the closing of the factory on bank holidays. In 1918, Cadbury Brothers established democratically elected Works Councils for men and women, which dealt with working conditions, health, safety, education, training, and the social life of the workers. Young employees were encouraged to attend night school and were allowed to leave work an hour early twice a week. Bournville College still provides training for school leavers and adults today. Around the turn of the last century, the Cadburys established medical and dental departments, and a pension fund was established in 1906.

The Cadbury family were involved in social reforms far beyond those directly impacting on their own business. John Cadbury led a campaign to ban the use of climbing boys to sweep chimneys and was also a leader in the struggle against animal cruelty, forming the Animals' Friend Society. This was a forerunner of the Royal Society for the Prevention of Cruelty to Animals. Members of the Cadbury family were actively involved as teachers in the adult school movement, to provide education to the working classes. By 1915, death and infant mortality rates in Bournville were half those of the city of Birmingham as a whole.

JOSEPH ROWNTREE

Under Joseph Rowntree's influence, the family company grew rapidly from 30 workers and by the end of the century it was an international concern with over 4,000 employees. (By this time the firm had diversified into non-chocolate products such as fruit-flavoured gum and jelly-based sweets.)

In 1883, after becoming the owner of the company, Joseph Rowntree devoted a considerable time to public work. During his life he served on the committee responsible for two Quaker schools in York and taught in an Adult School on Sundays, played a leading role in the establishment of the York Public Library and provided a park in York as a memorial to those killed during the First World War.

SEEBOHM ROWNTREE

Joseph's son, Benjamin Seebohm Rowntree, who joined the family business, wrote a book entitled *Poverty, a Study of Town Life*, which further influenced Joseph's desire to improve the quality of his employees' lives. He provided a library in the factory and free education for workers under 17. A social welfare officer, free doctor and dentist were also provided for the workforce. The Rowntrees were particularly concerned for the welfare and moral well-being of the women and girls employed to sort, decorate and pack the confectionery. In 1891, therefore, a Lady Welfare Supervisor was appointed to oversee the behaviour of female employees, who at this time could be as young as 13. Factory rules enforced what was seen as 'appropriate behaviour' for women workers, as well as encouraging maximum production.

By 1950 women constituted over half of the Rowntrees' workforce, which numbered around 7,000. Women were crucial to the business. Working hours varied and could be different for men and women, with a short evening shift, for example, which was introduced to increase production after the Second World War. It was designed to appeal to working mothers.

HOUSES AND PENSIONS

The Rowntrees' also provided practical help for the poor and in 1901 he purchased 123 acres at New Earswick, to build houses for low-income families. The first houses were finished in 1904. He also donated £10,000 in 1906 to establish a Pension Fund for his workers. One of his main innovations was to give the workers a say in the appointment of their immediate supervisors. A bit of a radical at the time, he was critical of the Anglican Church for what he considered to be its lack of interest in dealing with social injustice. He was also in favour of abolishing the House of Lords, an institution that he believed was hampering social progress.

FRENCH CHOCOLATE

French chocolate-making in the 19th century owes much to their love of chocolate, which was made famous by characters such as Queen Marie Antoinette and Napoleon Bonaparte.

DEBAUVE AND GALLAIS

Sulpice Debauve, a pharmacist and apothecary to King Louis XVI, before the monarch lost his head in the Revolution, opened his first chocolate shop on the left bank of the River Seine in Paris in 1800. Debauve's chocolate creations and innovations were immediately praised by the most influential figures in France and his business quickly expanded. By 1804 he had more than 60 shops throughout France. In 1823, he was joined by his nephew, Antoine Gallais, and the firm became known as Debauve and Gallais.

Debauve and Gallais obviously kept influential people happy with their products during a turbulent time in France. They were later appointed the official chocolatier of Louis XVIII and the House of Bourbon, Charles X and Louis Philippe. They also had a following within the Russian court, where the tsars traditionally favoured 99% cocoa, dark chocolates as an accompaniment to their strongest vodka. Among other illustrious fans were Brillat-Savarin (whose influence is still felt in the culinary world today), Proust, Baudelaire and Hugo. During the following years they developed trademark blue and grey colours. There was a coat of arms with seal of appointment as official purveyors to the French court. Special products included *Boite Frivoles* and *Croquamandes*. Today, Debauve & Gallais still enjoys a cult following and is considered one of the finest chocolate makers in the world.

NAPOLEON BONAPARTE
The French Emperor Napoleon insisted that wine from the Chambertin vineyard in Burgundy, as well as chocolate, was made available during military campaigns. He was a true fan of chocolate but, due to its precious nature, he didn't let just anyone get their hands on it, so the distribution of chocolate was apparently limited to himself and his senior military advisers. Napoleon is said to have drunk a cup of chocolate every night to restore the body and soul. Debauve & Gallais were the Emperor's sole provider of chocolate.

CARÊME
Marie-Antoine Carême (1784–1833) was one of the most famous French chefs of the 19th century. He was also the chef of Talleyrand, Prince de Bénévant, and chef to Emperor Napoleon and then to the Russian and Austrian emperors. He also worked sometimes with Auguste Gallais.

CROQUAMANDES
Carême, Debauve and Gallais often worked together. It seemed that the idea of *Croquamandes*, which are delicately caramelised almonds coated with dark chocolate, came from a discussion between the Emperor and Carême regarding the celebrations after the Friedland victory in June 1807. Debauve quickly made this new idea a reality and delivered the first *Croquamandes* to the Emperor. He was so glad that, some days later, he offered some *Croquamandes* with a cup of hot chocolate to the Maréchal Lefebvre in celebration of his enthroning as the Duke of Gdansk. This ensured that the names and reputations of the chocolatiers grew across Europe.

BISSINGER
The Bissinger family began creating their fine delicacies in 17th-century Paris, when European nobility, heads of state, Ludwig of Bavaria and the Rothschilds were all

loyal Bissinger enthusiasts. Bissinger's confections were once enjoyed by King Louis XIV and were given by Napoleon Bonaparte to his beloved Josephine upon his return from battle. Karl Frederic Bissinger was named the *Confiseur Imperial*, for excellence in the confectionery arts, by Emperor Louis Napoleon.

SWISS CHOCOLATE

During the 19th century increased production lowered the price of cacao beans, and technological improvements as well as creative interpretation, new roasting techniques and the spread of innovation all helped to develop the chocolate industry.

In 1819 the first Swiss chocolatier, François Louis Cailler, opened a chocolate factory (his second) in a former mill on Lake Geneva, using machinery he had developed himself. He had learned the trade in Italy. Twenty years later he sold this factory to Daniel Peter, who invented milk chocolate. Many of the early swiss chocolate-makers are still household names.

MILK CHOCOLATE
In 1879, after years of experimenting, Daniel Peter put the first milk chocolate on the market. He found a way of combining cocoa powder, cocoa butter and sugar with dried milk. Peter had tried repeatedly to produce the perfect chocolate bar during the 1860s, but he couldn't manage to produce a smooth enough mix of milk and chocolate. In 1867, Henri Nestlé, also Swiss, was working on a concentrated infant food formula, or baby milk. This required a way of treating milk so that it would not spoil while in storage but could be quickly reconstituted for use. A sweetened, condensed milk turned out to be perfect for Peter's purposes, as the low water content made it possible to mix it with the chocolate. By 1879, Peter and Nestlé had joined to form a company and Nestlé became one of the largest food producers in the world.

Also in 1879, Rudolphe Lindt of Bern, invented 'conching'. This is a way of heating and rolling chocolate to refine it. The conching machine was a shell-shaped granite bed, over which rollers moved back and forth to grind the chocolate liquor, sugar and milk into a paste. This paste was smoother than had ever been achieved before. After chocolate has been conched for 72 hours and has more cocoa butter added to it, the result is a fondant which melts in your mouth. Soon, conching became adopted as a standard step in the chocolate-making process, either with or without milk. Originally, the friction of the rollers heated the paste as they ground it, which meant that roasting the beans first could be eliminated. Modern conching machine rollers are cooled so that the roasting time can be controlled as much as possible.

SUCHARD

In 1825, Philippe Suchard opened a confectionery shop in Neuchâtel, Switzerland. A year later he set up his chocolate factory and his business grew rapidly. Suchard marketed at world expositions, most memorably in 1876, when an entire chalet in the Swiss mountains was dismantled and reconstructed in Paris to show visitors the company's products. By 1883, Suchard's company was the largest Swiss producer of chocolate, accounting for half of the total Swiss production. In 1901, the company combined a recipe with milk and chocolate was given the name *Milka*. The packaging reflected the new Art Nouveau movement, displaying lilac as the trademark colour and reflecting the world of the Alps through an illustration of a cow. Today, the lilac *Milka* cow has become so interwoven into popular culture in Germany that apparently some German school children, when asked to draw a farm scene, have been known to colour the cows lilac.

TOBLERONE

By 1900, Switzerland had taken over the lead in world chocolate manufacture. Spain, where chocolate was first introduced to Europeans, fell behind. Germany consumed the most per head, followed by the United States, France and Great Britain. Ten years later, after winning countless medals at international exhibitions, Swiss Chocolate had become a national institution.

Jean Tobler began production of handmade confections in Bern in the 1860s, but didn't start to make chocolate himself until 1899. His son, Theodore and a cousin entered the business and in 1908 a triangular shaped bar of almond chocolate was first marketed. The name Toblerone, was a mix of the family name and the Italian word *Torrone*, meaning a honey, nut nougat. The triangular-shaped pieces are said to have been inspired by the Swiss mountains, in particular the Matterhorn. (As a teacher, I found the box provided the perfect example of an equilateral, triangular prism and the perfect reason to buy the boxes: for maths purposes only, of course!)

In 1913, Jules Sechaud of Montreux, Switzerland, invented the machinery that enabled the process for filling chocolates.

BELGIAN CHOCOLATE

Belgian chocolates have always been associated with quality ingredients and came to the forefront at the beginning of the 20th century. Most Belgian chocolate is still made by hand in small shops, using original equipment.

NEUHAUS PRALINES

Belgian chocolate has been popular since the 18th century, but a new process created by Jean Neuhaus increased its popularity. Neuhaus was from Switzerland, but set up business in Brussels in 1857. With his brother-in-law, a pharmacist, he opened a 'pharmaceutical confectioner's', making cough sweets, liquorice for stomach complaints and bars of bitter chocolate. In 1912, he used a special version of chocolate, called couverture, as a hard chocolate shell for what he called 'pralines'. These are not the same as the nutty, sugary chocolates or sweets offered in some sweetshops today. Belgian chocolate pralines could be filled with a variety of flavoured nougats or creams, such as coffee, hazelnut, fruit or more chocolate. Few other chocolatiers at the time could copy Neuhaus's recipes.

One technical advantage is the storage of *couverture* before use. After the cacao beans are ground and mixed with sugar and cocoa butter, they are smoothed out through tempering, or careful addition of heat. Most chocolate companies receive their chocolate in solid form, which needs to be reheated in order to be used. Belgian chocolate companies often receive their chocolate in heated tankers. Because the chocolate has not cooled, it retains much more of the aroma. Neuhaus chocolate allowed for softer, smoother fillings and creams inside. Previously, fillings had to be of a certain consistency to allow handling and chocolate coating. With the advent of the hard shell coating, fillings could be of nearly any consistency.

LEONIDAS
Leonidas was founded in Belgium in 1910 by a Greek, Leonidas Kesdekidis. He arrived in Brussels as a member of the Greek delegation of the United States for the International Exposition and won the Bronze Medal. In 1935, Leonidas's nephew, Basile Kesdekidis, joined the business and incorporated the logo showing the effigy of the Greek warrior Leonidas, King of Sparta.

AMERICAN CHOCOLATE

It seems a bit of an irony that chocolate took so long to make its way to North America, especially when so much of the cacao originally came from Central America. Well kept secrets bear much of the responsibility. It was 1755 before chocolate finally reached the north of the continent. One of the earliest enterprises was Baker's Chocolate, in Massachusetts, which opened in 1765.

GHIRARDELLI
Domingo Ghirardelli emigrated to Uruguay from his native Italy, in 1837, to establish a business in coffee and chocolate. He moved around for a few years and then, in 1849, set off for California, where he had his eye on the Gold Rush. Apparently, he didn't waste much time hunting for gold, but became a merchant, selling general supplies to the miners, originally from a tent. He opened

a second shop and despite this one being burned down in 1851, he survived in the business and opened his first factory to make chocolate in 1852. In 1865 he was credited with developing the Broma Process, whereby chocolate hung in a warmed room allowed the cocoa butter to drip out.

GUITTARD

In the 1850s, Frenchman Etienne Guittard, an experienced chocolatier, left France for America. During the California Gold Rush he tried to trade French chocolate for mining supplies. He discovered, however, that the wealthy miners were willing to pay handsomely for the treat of delicious chocolate. He sailed back to France, where he worked until he could afford to buy his own chocolate-making equipment. In 1868, he returned to San Francisco and opened Guittard Chocolate. San Francisco became one of the great chocolate manufacturing centres in America. Today, Guittard, under control of its founder's great-grandson, is the largest, privately owned chocolate company in the United States.

CULTURAL CHOCOLATE

In 1862 the Baker's Chocolate Company obtained the rights to use the painting *La Belle Chocolatiere* by the Swiss artist Jean-Etienne Liotard. The painting shows the wife of Prince Dietrichstein, an Austrian nobleman, as a maid serving chocolate. Apparently, in 1745 the Prince stopped by a chocolate shop in Vienna to try a new chocolate drink people were talking about. His waitress was Anna Baltauf, daughter of an impoverished knight. Prince Dietrichstein was taken by the young lady and, despite objections from his family, he soon married her. As a wedding gift, Prince Dietrichstein commissioned a portrait of his wife, posing in her 18th-century chocolate server's costume.

HERSHEY

In 1876, Milton Snavely Hershey founded a sweet, or 'candy' shop in Philadelphia, which failed six years later. Hershey returned to Pennsylvania, where he founded the Lancaster Caramel Company, whose use of fresh milk in caramels proved successful. Milton S Hershey opened the world's first modern chocolate factory and built a model town, to provide employees and their families with an attractive place to live, work and play, at about the same time as the Quaker families in Britain were developing their philanthropic business enterprises. Hershey sold the caramel business in 1900 to concentrate on perfecting his milk chocolate bars.

In 1907, Hershey introduced small, flat-bottomed conical-shaped pieces of chocolate named 'Hershey's Kisses'. Initially they were individually wrapped by hand in squares of foil. After the introduction of machine wrapping in 1921 simplified the process, he added a small paper ribbon to the top of the package, to indicate that it was a genuine Hershey product. He also opened Hershey Park in 1907 for workers and their families and also built a zoo. During the Depression he created jobs in the building trade through construction of a stadium, sports arena, theatre and hotel. In 1909 he founded the Hershey Industrial School for Orphan Boys and a trust to provide funding.

Hershey's business grew rapidly, despite his refusal to advertise his products.

COCOA EXCHANGE
Located at the World Trade Centre, the New York Cocoa Exchange was launched in 1925, so that buyers and sellers could get together for transactions. Chocolate had finally become big business.

TO INFINITY AND BEYOND
In 1938, the US government recognised chocolate's role in the Allied Armed Forces. It allocated shipping space for the importation of cocoa beans, so that production of chocolate could increase, giving the armed forces access to chocolate on active service. Hershey was the first to experiment with the use of solid vegetable fats instead of pure cocoa, which raised the melting point of a chocolate bar. This enabled his chocolates to withstand the heat of American summers and shipments to troops during the Second World War. Chocolate has even been taken into space as part of the diet of US astronauts.

Where Does Cocoa Come From?

This section explains all about the cacao plant and its family and also a little about the worldwide production of cocoa. Producing the cacao beans is the first stage in the production of chocolate, which is covered in a later section.

QUITE A FAMILY

Cocoa comes from the cacao bean which is produced on pods on a cacao tree. The cacao tree belongs to the family *Sterculiaceae*. This family of plants has about 12 genera of tropical and subtropical trees, shrubs and herbs. Five of these genera are found in the southern United States, Central America and north of South America.

The leaves of the *Sterculiaceae* are divided into leaflets and radiate from a point, like fingers. The flowers are either solitary or clustered, according to variety, and there are three to five sepals and either five or no petals.

COLA

As well as including cacao (*Theobroma cacao*) in its ranks, it also includes, interestingly enough, cola (*Cola nitida* and *Cola acuminate*). These colas contain the flavourings and stimulants used in the manufacture of cola drinks. Suddenly the effects of cacao in a variety of health benefits begin to make more sense. Now read on for more revelations!

GUM

Another member of the family, *Sterculia urens* gives karaya gum. I was interested to learn that karaya gum is used in the pharmaceutical industry for two main purposes: as a laxative and also as a dental adhesive. We'd best not get those two confused!

Karaya gum is also used as a substitute for gum tragacanth, a viscous, odourless, tasteless, water-soluble mixture of polysaccharides. It is obtained from sap which is drained from the root of the plant and dried. The gum seeps from the plant and can be powdered. The gum is occasionally used as a stiffener in textiles and historically has been used as a herbal remedy for such conditions as coughs and diarrhoea. As a paste it has been used as a topical treatment for burns and it is used in pharmaceuticals and foods as an emulsifier, thickener and a stabiliser. It is also the traditional binder used in the making of artist's pastels, as it does not stick to itself when dry.

ORNAMENTALS

Some species are cultivated as ornamentals, especially the bottle tree (*Brachychiton*) and the Chinese parasol tree (*Firmiyana*), the flannel bush (*Fremontodendron*), Dombeya (*Dombeya*) and Sterculia (*Sterculia*).

Members of the *Sterculiaceae* family are specially adapted for insect pollination. Sterculia have dark purple or chocolate-coloured flowers with an unpleasant smell which attracts flies to help with pollination. *Theobroma cacao* is pollinated by, amongst other things, thrips, ants, midges and aphids; just about anything, really.

By the way, cocoa is not to be confused with the coca plant, which is used to create cocaine.

THEOBROMA CACAO

Theobroma cacao is a small evergreen tree, native to the deep tropical region of the Americas. It grows 4–8 m tall (15–26 ft). There are competing theories about the origins of the cacao tree, although recent studies seem to show that the plant originated in the Amazon and was distributed by man throughout Central America.

The plant is found growing wild in the low foothills of the Andes at elevations of around 200–400 m (650–1,300 ft) in the Amazon and Orinoco river basins. Cacao needs a humid climate, with regular rainfall and good soil. Cacao trees resemble apple trees and they are carefully pruned so that pods can be more easily harvested. The leaves are alternate and 10–40 cm (4–16 in) long and 5–20 cm (2–8 in) broad. Small flowers are produced in clusters directly on the trunk and older branches. They are small, at about 1–2 cm (½ to 1 in) in diameter, with a pink calyx. Flowers are produced all year round. There may be as many as 6,000 on a tree but only a small proportion of these flowers, maybe only about 20, develop into fruit, over a period of about five months.

GROWING CONDITIONS
Cacao trees are fairly difficult to grow and choosy about the right conditions. They will only grow in the tropics, 20° south and 20° north of the equator. They like some overhead shade, so grow as an understorey tree. This allows the plant to be grown mixed with other crops in the rainforest, at an altitude of 400–700 m (1,300–2,300 ft). The temperature for cacao trees cannot drop below 15°C (60°F) without damaging the tree.

YIELD
The cacao tree yields its first crop at three to four years old. Adult plants, after about 10 years, can produce from 130–450 kg (300–1,000 lb) of cocoa per acre, for about 50 years. It takes 20–25 pods to get around a kilo or 2 lb of raw cacao.

BEANS AND PODS
The fruit, called a cacao pod, is like a pendulous egg and can be 15–30 cm (6–12 in) long and up to 8–10 cm (7–9 in) wide. As it ripens it turns from yellow to golden red, to brown, and weighs about 500 g (1 lb). Each pod contains from 20 to 50 seeds or beans, embedded in a white pulp. Each seed contains a significant amount of fat (40–50% as cocoa butter). The most active constituent is theobromine, a compound similar to caffeine, which you can find out about in a later section.

BEAN VARIETIES
There are three main varieties of cacao beans that are used to make chocolate.

- *CRIOLLO*
  Criollo is the rarest and most expensive cocoa on the market and is native to Central America, the Caribbean islands and the northern tier of South American states. It is also grown in Indonesia. The purity of criollos may have been affected over the

years by cultivation and they are particularly difficult to grow. They were the beans grown by the Mayan people in pre-Colombian times. They are vulnerable to a variety of environmental threats and not as hardy as other varieties. They produce low yields of cacao per tree in softer pods containing 20–30 white or pale purple beans. The flavour of Criollo is said to be unique. It is described as mild yet complex, with a light chocolate flavour, but rich secondary flavours of long duration. Only 10% of chocolate is made from Criollo beans

- *FORASTERO*

Forastero is the name given to a large group of wild and cultivated cacaos, most likely native to the Amazon basin. The African cacao crop is entirely of the Forastero variety, mostly *Amelonado*. Brazilian crops are also mostly of this type. They are significantly hardier, vigorous and of higher yield than Criollo. The smooth pods contain about 30 pale to deep purple beans. Forastero cocoas are said to be stronger in flavour, but have a short duration of taste. They don't have secondary flavours, with the exception of the *Nacional* or the *Arriba* varieties. It has been estimated that 80% of chocolate is made using Forastero beans.

- *TRINITARIO*

Trinitario is a natural hybrid of Criollo and Forastero. Trinitario, unsurprisingly, given its name, originated in Trinidad after an introduction of Forastero to the local Criollo crop. It is considered a lower grade variety and is grown mainly in the Caribbean, Cameroon and Papua New Guinea. The hard pods are variable in colour and they contain 30 or more beans. Trinitario beans account for 10% of chocolate manufactured.

Nearly all the cacao produced over the last 50 years is of the Forastero or Trinitario varieties.

CULTIVATION
New plants can be produced by propagation from cuttings or graftings, but are produced more cheaply from seeds.

Seeds germinate at maturity, and are viable for germination for only a short time. They may be stored for about three months if the moisture content is kept at 50%. Soon after picking, the pulp is removed from the pods and the seeds, which are planted in shaded nursery beds or baskets. After a few months the young plants can be transplanted, when about 60 cm (2 ft) tall, into shaded fields at about 3 m (10 ft) intervals. Spacing is often closer at elevations above 300 m (1,000 feet).

The trees need to remain shaded for three years. Cacao is often intercropped with other trees, such as bananas, plantains, rubber, oil palm or coconut. These can be permanent or temporary shade trees. Irrigation is sometimes used, but ditches are provided to prevent excess water. In Asia where large plantations have been developed, cacao trees and coconut trees have been planted together and both crops are harvested commercially. Another method is to thin out forest trees and to plant cacao trees between established trees.

HARVESTING

Harvesting cacao beans needs to be done delicately. Although fruits mature throughout the year, usually only two harvests are made. In West Africa, the main harvest begins in September, continuing until December or even February. A second, smaller harvest is made in May and June. Each tree will yield 20–30 pods per year.

Firstly, the pods are collected and left to mellow on the ground. They are cut from the trees with a curved knife on a long pole. The pods are harvested green through preference, rather than when red or orange, because they have a better flavour. The pod has a rough, leathery skin. Overripe pods are often used for industrial chocolate manufacture. The pods are then cracked open and the beans, together with their surrounding pulp, are removed from the pod and placed in piles or leaf-lined bins to ferment for anything from two to eight days. At this time they change colour from purple to brown. This process gives the beans their familiar chocolate taste. The beans must then be quickly dried to prevent mould growth.

The pulp liquefies as it ferments and trickles away, leaving the beans behind, although this liquefied pulp is used by some cacao producing countries to distill alcoholic spirits. This fermenting or sweating is important for the quality of the beans, which originally have a strong bitter taste. The crop may be ruined if the process is interrupted. If underfermented the beans will taste like raw potatoes (not to be recommended!) and become susceptible to mildew.

DRYING
This is usually done by spreading the beans out in the sun or by roasting. During drying the beans lose about half of their weight and nearly all of their moisture. Natural drying is preferred so that no other flavours from smoke or oil interfere with the chocolate flavour. Beans are spread out over a large surface and constantly raked. In large plantations, this is done on huge trays. Smaller plantations may dry their harvest on smaller trays or on cowhides. Sometimes the beans are trodden in bare feet and shuffled about, and sometimes red clay mixed with water is sprinkled over the beans to improve the colour, polish, and protect against moulds during shipments.

WORLD SOURCES OF CACAO

Cacao is cultivated over an estimated 70,000 km^2 (27,000 sq m) worldwide. Roughly 70% of the world's cocoa today is produced in Western Africa, with nearly 40% coming from the Côte d'Ivoire alone. Ghana, Nigeria and Cameroon also contribute to this total. Ghana produces about 15–20% and Indonesia produce just under 15%. The rest is produced from other countries. The Americas, led by Brazil and Ecuador, produce about 10%.

Cocoa farmers in many countries lack information on production and marketing practices to help them improve their livelihoods. Over 3,400,000 tonnes of cacao were grown in 2005–6. The global production has increased by over 130% in the last 30 years. Poor rainfall, however, and pod borer disease in Asia, the Americas and other regions have led to a decline in recent times.

An estimated 45 million people in the world rely on cocoa for a livelihood.

Like many food producers, individual cacao farmers are at the mercy of world markets. The price of raw cacao can vary a huge amount in the space of a few years. While investors trading in cocoa can dump shares at will, individual cacao farmers cannot increase production or abandon trees at anywhere near the same pace. Many farmers are subsistence farmers, with whole families supported by the cacao crop.

Many are having to work harder and longer for less money. The market price of commodities frequently drops below the cost of producing them.

International trade may not seem to be the topic you expected in a book on a luxury foodstuff, but when commodity prices fall there is a catastrophic impact on the lives of small-scale producers, forcing debt, loss of land and their homes.

WEST AFRICA
In West Africa there are more than two million cocoa farms, stretching across tens of thousands of square miles of rural geography. When cocoa prices drop, farmers in West Africa sometimes cut costs by using child or slave labour. It has been alleged that an estimated 90% of cocoa farms in Côte d'Ivoire have used some form of slave labour in order to remain viable. When it emerged that children were being harmed in the growing of cocoa in West Africa a protocol was set up by the industry to try to ensure that cocoa is grown responsibly, without the worst forms of child labour or forced adult labour. But progress has been slow, due partly to political divisions and instability. Through the efforts of a number of charities, including the World Cocoa Foundation and government development agencies, the protocol is now moving forward, especially in Ghana. In 2002 there were still an estimated 109,000 children working on cocoa farms in Côte d'Ivoire.

FAIRTRADE

The Fairtrade Foundation was established in 1992 by CAFOD, Christian Aid, New Consumer, Oxfam, Traidcraft and the World Development Movement. These founding organisations were later joined by the Women's Institute. Fairtrade now operates 21 national labelling initiatives across Europe, Japan, North America, Mexico, Australia and New Zealand. The goods involved include coffee, drinking chocolate, chocolate bars, orange juice, tea, honey, sugar and bananas.

Development agencies encouraged farmers by buying at better prices and helping them to organise and market their produce directly through charity shops and catalogues. The charities offered consumers the opportunity to buy products which were bought on the basis of a fair trade. However, this fair trade remains a tiny percentage of the total trade, although consumers are becoming more aware of the problems the cocoa producers face. Fair trade goods are now more readily available in supermarkets, where most people do their shopping.

The UK organic chocolate company Green & Black's — who are now owned by Cadbury — created a chocolate bar called Maya Gold which subsequently earned the company the UK's first Fairtrade mark.

SOUTH-EAST ASIA

A relative newcomer to cacao farming, South-East Asia has emerged as a cacao grower for the worldwide market in the past 20 years. In Indonesia, Papua New Guinea, Malaysia, the Philippines and Vietnam, thousands of small cacao farmers, with average farms of around 2 acres, produce thousands of tonnes of cacao annually. The Malaysian cacao industry, which started its commercial planting in the early 1950s, experienced a growth accompanied by high prices of cacao in the 1970s and 1980s. The cultivated area expanded until 1989, but has since declined, after a peak in the production of cacao beans in 1994. The average South-East Asian cacao farm supports a family of five to seven people. World Cocoa Foundation Programmes in South-East Asia help farmers earn more for their cacao crop through improved productivity, reduced crop loss and better farming practices. They help farmers to sell their product in bulk and negotiate a better price for their cacao.

THE AMERICAS AND THE CARIBBEAN

A surge in demand for good quality chocolate over the past two years has led to an increased price for the very best cacao beans, where traders have paid ten times the world cocoa price in recent years. Isolated growers producing a high enough yield for buyers are in great demand. Abandoned plantations with nearly pure criollo species across the rainforests of the Dominican Republic, Ecuador, Mexico, Jamaica and Trinidad have excited producers at the luxury end of the market, such as chocolatiers in Europe. The beans of Chuao, an isolated village hidden deep in the northern Venezuelan forests, are said to be the best in the world. Only 20 tonnes are produced each year, but they command high prices and world recognition for Chuao chocolate at the Academy of Chocolate awards. Life for the villagers of the Chuao cooperative, who harvest three times a year, is presently a million miles from the conditions in West Africa. The beans are processed by Amedei in Tuscany and find their way to the palates of the world's elite.

WORLD COCOA-PRODUCING COUNTRIES

- **CARIBBEAN PRODUCERS**
  Cuba
  Dominica
  Dominican Republic
  Grenada
  Haiti
  Jamaica
  St Lucia
  Trinidad & Tobago

- **CENTRAL AND SOUTH AMERICA**
Belize
Brazil
Colombia
Costa Rica
Ecuador
Guatemala
Honduras
Mexico
Nicaragua
Panama
Peru
Republic of Suriname
Venezuela

- **AFRICA**
Cameroon
Côte d'Ivoire
Democratic Republic of São Tome & Principe
Ghana
Madagascar
Nigeria
Sierra Leone
Tanzania

- **S E ASIA**
Indonesia
Malaysia
Papua New Guinea
Philippines
Republic of Vanuatu
Sri Lanka
Vietnam

- **WORLD COCOA PRODUCTION, 2005—6**

Ivory Coast	38%
Ghana	21%
Indonesia	13%
Nigeria	5%
Malaysia	5%
Ecuador	4%
Brazil	3%
Cameroon	1%
Others	10%

What is Chocolate?

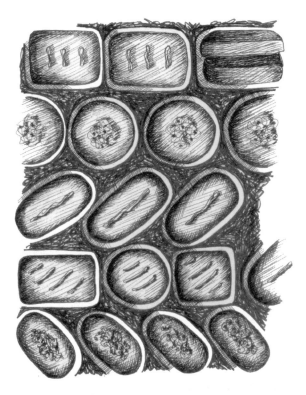

DEFINITIONS

CACAO is the dried and partially fermented fatty seed of the cacao tree from which chocolate is made.

COCOA POWDER is made by grinding cacao seeds and removing the cocoa butter from the dark, bitter cacao solids. There are two types of unsweetened baking cocoa available. These are natural cocoa and Dutch-process cocoa. Both are made by pulverising partially defatted chocolate liquor and removing nearly all the cocoa butter: between 8% and 36% of the cocoa butter remains. In the UK cocoa sold for beverages must contain at least 20% cocoa butter.

Natural cocoa is light in colour and somewhat acidic, with a pH of 5.2—5.8 and a strong chocolate flavour. It is frequently used in recipes which call for bicarbonate of soda. As bicarbonate of soda is an alkali, combining it with natural cocoa creates a leavening action, allowing the batter to rise during baking. There's a whole section with cake and biscuit recipes later on. Another curious fact about cocoa and the effect of combining it with bicarbonate of soda is that it causes a reddening of the cake, but I'm digressing.

Dutch-process cocoa, as first applied by Van Houten, in the Netherlands in 1828, is processed with alkali to neutralise the natural cocoa acids. Potassium carbonate or sodium carbonate may be used. It is slightly milder in taste, with a deeper and warmer colour than natural cocoa, caused by the altering of the pH. It is frequently used on the continent, for chocolate drinks such as hot chocolate, thanks to its ready blending with liquids. Unfortunately, Dutch processing destroys most of the flavonols present in cocoa, which are good for you. You can find out more in the health benefits section.

CHOCOLATE can be defined as any product made primarily of cocoa solids and cocoa fat. Different flavours of chocolate can be obtained by varying the time and temperature when roasting the beans. Adjusting the quantities of the cocoa solids and fat, or adding non-chocolate ingredients, also changes the taste and the price.

As chocolate is used in a vast number of other foods, any change in the cost of making it has a huge impact on the industry. Reducing cocoa solid content, or substituting cocoa fat with a non-cocoa fat, reduces the production costs.

The definition of chocolate has posed some problems within the EU, with disputes covering several ingredients, including the types of fat used and quantity of cocoa. In 1999, the issue was resolved by allowing up to 5% of the content of chocolate to be comprised of one of five alternatives to cocoa butter, which are: illipe, sal, shea (all types of shorea palm), palm oil or mango kernel. These all provide soft vegetable fat.

COCOA BUTTER is also called theobroma oil. It is a pale yellow vegetable fat and has a mild chocolate flavour. As well as being used in chocolate confections, it is widely used in the pharmaceutical industry for ointments and in a range of toiletries. The value of cocoa butter in these contexts derives from the fact that it is brittle at room temperature but melts at just below body temperature. (See a later section for more details). Cocoa butter is one of the most stable fats and contains antioxidants which allow for a long storage life.

CHOCOLATE LIQUOR When dried beans are transported from the plantation they are cleaned, roasted and graded. Next, the shells are removed to extract the nib or kernel. Finally, the nibs are ground, forming a paste and releasing and melting the cocoa butter, to produce chocolate liquor. Find out what happens next, below.

CHOCOLATE-MAKERS use harvested cacao beans and other ingredients to produce couverture chocolate.

CHOCOLATIERS use the finished couverture, or bulk chocolate, to make chocolate goods and confectionery.

COUVERTURE The finest plain dark chocolate couvertures contain a minimum of 70% cocoa solids and butter, whereas milk chocolate usually contains up to 50%. High-quality white chocolate couvertures only contain about

33% cocoa. Some chocolate contains much less cocoa, which can be as little as 7%, and fats other than cocoa butter. Some chocolate-makers feel that these products should not be classed as chocolate, given the low or virtually non-existent cocoa content. It is much cheaper to make a chocolaty taste by adding more sugar and vegetable fat, so profits can increase faster that way. It also means that a lot of consumers, especially children, grow to love the sugar rather than the chocolate taste. Still, it is one way of keeping the children away from your best Belgian chocs or finest dark, cocoa butter rich fix! Not a healthy option, however.

How Chocolate is Made

THE CHOCOLATE-MAKING PROCESS

FERMENTED, DRIED CACAO BEANS

Cleaning
Shelling
Winnowing
Roasting

LIQUOR FOR PROCESSING

Cocoa cake	Cocoa butter
Milling	for refining in
Sieving	confectionery
Cocoa powder	and other
	industries

LIQUOR FOR CHOCOLATE

Blending
Mixing with sugar, milk
Refining
Conching
Tempering
Liquid chocolate/couverture

Stored as liquid, moulded or
for covering products

After arriving at the processing works or chocolate factory, the cocoa beans go through a great deal before they're ready to eat as chocolate.

ROASTING

After the beans have been harvested they need to be cleaned ready for roasting. This dries and browns the beans and develops the flavour. Fermentation has already produced some of the flavours, which now need to be enhanced. This is a delicate process because, if not completed correctly, the beans will be spoiled. The amount of time for roasting depends on the variety of beans and the type of product they will be made into.

Pre-roasting is more productive, but some varieties of beans can be damaged by the sudden heat. The beans are heated with infra-red heaters or hot air, to separate the nibs or kernels from the shell, and then roasted between 100°C (212°F) and 150°C (300°F) for 20 to 40 minutes. Another method is to roast and remove shells all at once. This is an older, more traditional method. Roasting is carried out in temperatures between 150°C and 160°C (300°F and 320°F) for 40 to 50 minutes.

SHELLING

After roasting — or during, if the pre-roasting method has been used — the beans are shelled to reveal the nibs. This involves a winnowing machine.

ALKALISATION

At this point the nibs are alkalised, usually with potassium carbonate, to develop the flavour and colour.

MILLING

This ensures pure grains of a similar size. Again, the process must be carried out carefully, otherwise friction can cause the beans to smoke or burn and the flavours will be altered or damaged.

REFINING

This converts the particles of bean into chocolate liquor, where the cocoa particles are suspended in cocoa butter.

There are three things that can be done with the chocolate liquor when it has been extracted:

- It can be hardened in moulds and sold as bitter or baking chocolate. Unsweetened chocolate is pure, unadulterated chocolate liquor. It has a strong, deep chocolate flavour.
- Most of the cocoa butter can be removed by pressing the liquor and then pulverising it, resulting in cocoa powder. There are several mechanisms for removing cocoa butter from chocolate liquor, including using hydraulic pressure and the Broma process (see below).
- Sugar and additional cocoa butter can be added to it to make eating chocolate. The varying quantities make different types of chocolate or couverture. The basic blends of ingredients for chocolate are dark, milk or white. Dark chocolate has the most cocoa liquor with sugar, cocoa butter and, sometimes, vanilla. In addition, milk chocolate includes, rather obviously, milk or milk powder and vanilla. White chocolate does not contain chocolate liquor.

BLENDING

Usually, an emulsifying agent such as soya lecithin is added, although some manufacturers use an artificial emulsifier derived from castor oil, that allows them to reduce the amount of cocoa butter while maintaining the same texture. The mixture travels through a series of rollers until a smooth paste is formed.

CONCHING

The penultimate process in chocolate-making is called conching, a process invented by Rudolphe Lindt of Berne, in 1879. A conche is not a shell but a container filled with metal beads, which act as grinders. The process helps to develop the flavour of the chocolate and aerates and emulsifies it further. The refined and blended chocolate mass is kept liquid by heat caused by friction. The temperature of the chocolate ranges from 54°C (130°F) to 88°C (190°F) and is closely monitored. Conching produces cocoa and sugar particles smaller than the tongue can detect, hence the smooth feel in the mouth.

The amount of time spent conching determines the final quality and smooth texture of the chocolate. High-quality chocolate is conched for about 72 hours but lesser grades get away with about four to six hours. After the process is complete, the chocolate mass is stored in tanks heated to approximately 45 to 50°C (113 to 122°F) until final processing takes place.

TEMPERING

This is the final process in making fine quality chocolate. It transforms liquid or semi-liquid chocolate into a solid. The uniform sheen of properly processed chocolate is the result of consistently small cocoa butter crystals, produced by the tempering process. Uncontrolled crystallisation of cocoa butter results in crystals of varying size, some or all of which may be large enough to be clearly seen. This causes the surface of the chocolate to appear mottled and dull, and causes the chocolate to crumble rather than snap when broken.

The fats in cocoa butter crystallise in six different forms, which all have different properties.

CRYSTAL MELTING TEMP	NOTES
17°C (63°F)	Soft, crumbly, melts too easily
21°C (70°F)	Soft, crumbly, melts too easily
26°C (78°F)	Firm, poor snap, melts too easily
28°C (82°F)	Firm, good snap, melts too easily
34°C (94°F)	Glossy, firm, best snap and just right
36°C (97°F)	Hard, takes weeks to form

This is beginning to sound a bit like Goldilocks. Only crystals that melt at 34°C (94°F) are just right. These crystals melt just below normal body temperature (37°C or 98.4°F) and make chocolate of a good appearance and texture that will not be lost over time.

THE GLAZED LOOK
In case you are interested in how this fantastic taste experience is achieved, read on. If not, fast forward a little.

- The chocolate is first heated to 45°C (113°F), to melt all six forms of crystals, and then it is cooled to about 27°C (80°F), allowing only two types of crystal to form in the short term.
- At this temperature, the chocolate is agitated to create many small crystal seeds, which will serve as nuclei to create small crystals in the chocolate.
- The chocolate is then heated to about 31°C (88°F), leaving just the right crystals. Any excessive heating will destroy the temper and this process will have to be repeated. That reminds me of a scene from *Chocolat*, by Joanna Harris, or the film version at least, starring Juliette Binoche.

Pause here for a chocolate-tasting moment!

Ways of tempering chocolate are by:
- Working the molten chocolate on a heat-absorbing surface, such as a stone slab. Thickening indicates the presence of sufficient crystal seeds. The chocolate is then gently warmed to working temperature.
- Introducing already tempered, solid seed chocolate into molten chocolate to 'inoculate' the liquid chocolate with crystals.

TEMPER, TEMPER
The modern way to monitor and temper chocolate is with a chocolate temper meter. These offer accuracy for the measurement of temper in a single, no-mess unit. The process involves filling a sample cup with chocolate, placing it in the unit and waiting for a printed and displayed temper result within minutes, so that

corrective action can be taken. This avoids everyone getting a bad temper!

THE BROMA PROCESS
Ghirardelli invented this in 1865, in the USA. It involved the fairly simple act of hanging a bag of raw cocoa in a warm room. The residue left can then be converted to ground cocoa and the cocoa butter is collected underneath. More cocoa butter is extracted this way than in the hydraulic press, so it makes it easier to dissolve the ground cocoa in liquids. Broma cocoa is even more intense than Dutch cocoa.

THE HYDRAULIC PRESS
This was invented in 1795 by a British inventor called Bramah. It was used to apply pressure to the cocoa, to extract the cocoa butter. You may be interested to know that amongst his other inventions were a type of flushing toilet, a beer pump and a type of lock. What more would you need?

WHERE DOES IT ALL END UP?
After processing, one-third of production remains as cocoa liquor and the rest is pressed to make cocoa butter and cocoa powder. The majority of the cocoa butter is used in chocolate production along with the cocoa liquor. Products usually need more cocoa butter adding to them than exists in the chocolate liquor. So, roughly two-thirds of bean production is used to make chocolate and one-third to make cocoa powder.

GRADES OF CHOCOLATE

DARK OR PLAIN CHOCOLATE
This is chocolate without milk as an additive. The USA calls this 'sweet chocolate', and requires a 15% concentration of chocolate liquor. European rules specify a minimum of 35% cocoa solids. Plain chocolate can be flavoured with vanilla, salt, chilli, spices or essential oils like orange.

MILK CHOCOLATE
This is chocolate with whole milk solids or condensed milk substituted for a proportion of the chocolate liquor. The USA requires a 10% concentration of chocolate liquor. EU regulations specify a minimum of 25% cocoa solids.

AERATED CHOCOLATE
With normal aeration, large bubbles are created in the chocolate mass. This obviously reduces the density of chocolate and alters its texture. The chocolate is usually aerated after tempering by using a specialised machine. Different methods can be used. For example, the chocolate can be subjected to a vacuum, causing small bubbles to expand, or gas can be injected into the chocolate under pressure to create the bubbles.

COUVERTURE
This is also known as bulk chocolate by chocolate-makers and chocolatiers.

SEMISWEET chocolate is often used for cooking purposes. It is a dark chocolate with a high, typically 50%, sugar content.

BITTERSWEET chocolate is chocolate liquor to which some sugar, typically 30%, has been added, along with more cocoa butter, vanilla and sometimes lecithin. It has less sugar and more liquor than semisweet chocolate, but the two are interchangeable in baking.

Bittersweet and semisweet chocolates are sometimes referred to as couverture, which must contain at least 32% cocoa butter. Many brands now print on the package the percentage of cocoa, as chocolate liquor and added cocoa butter, contained. The higher the percentage of cocoa, the less sweet the chocolate will be. This is good news for diabetics, like me. I can justify a little treat now and again and can only eat really good quality chocolate! The intensity of the chocolate flavour is so good that I only need one square to satisfy the chocolate craving, when it comes.

Popular brands used by professional pastry chefs and often sold in gourmet and speciality food stores include: Amedei Tuscany Chuao, Lindt & Sprüngli, Scharffen Berger, Cacao Barry, Callebaut, and Guittard, Green and Black and some Fairtrade chocolate. There are many more. These chocolates contain a high percentage of cocoa (sometimes 70% or more) and have a total fat content of 30 to 40%.

OTHER, ADDED BITS AND PIECES
GLUCOSE SYRUP is manufactured mainly from corn. Different compositions of glucose syrup can be made, but it has a high water content which affects the flowing properties of chocolate. It is normally used in fondants and toffees.

SUGAR OR SUCROSE gives taste and texture to chocolate. Replacing sucrose with the naturally occurring fruit sugar, fructose, produces chocolate with a different texture and sweetness to sugared chocolate. Sugar alcohols such as sorbitol can be used to give mass, volume and texture in sugar-free chocolate. These generally give a different sweetness and taste to sucrose and they tend to be used in combination with bulking agents, such as polydextrose and inulin. These bulking agents produce a warm soft feeling in the mouth. Sweetness can also be achieved by using high-intensity sweeteners such as aspartame and saccharin. It's probably a good idea to read the contents labels if you can't have sugar.

SUGAR FREE chocolate methods have to be altered, as some of the sweeteners have lower melting points, therefore conching temperatures have to be lower. Also, some pick up moisture causing an increase in viscosity during tempering and moulding. I'm sticking to small quantities of ordinary, good quality chocolate.

VEGETABLE FAT Up to 5% vegetable fat or Cocoa Butter Equivalents (CBEs) is permitted in chocolate under EU regulations, although some countries don't allow any at all. So far there has been little impact on the cocoa market and very few manufacturers have used CBEs in their recipes.

A confection combining cocoa with vegetable fat, replacing cocoa butter completely, is also made. This substitute has been described as substandard and is sometimes used for coating 'chocolate' or biscuit bars. Some countries called chocolate with added vegetable fat 'vegelate', although this is not an officially used term. Much of the 'white chocolate' around apparently may have nothing from a cocoa bush in its make up. The result is often a poor tasting, overly sweet product, which isn't chocolate at all.

LECITHIN is used commercially as a natural emulsifier and lubricant, from pharmaceuticals to protective coverings. Lecithin is the emulsifier that keeps cocoa and cocoa butter in a chocolate bar from separating. A major source of lecithin is soybean oil, but a gradual shift to other sources, such as sunflower oil, is taking place.

VANILLA was cultivated by pre-Colombian inhabitants of Central America. The Aztecs used it as a flavouring for chocolate. Vanillin was first isolated in 1858 by Nicolas-Theodore Gobley, who evaporated a vanilla extract to dryness, and then recrystallised it. Since then, synthetic vanillin has become more prevalent.

BY-PRODUCTS OF COCOA
Many different sorts of products can be derived from cacao. The husks of cacao pods and the pulp surrounding the beans and the cacao bean shells can be used for:
- Animal feed. Dry 100% cacao pod husk can made into pellets and used as animal feed.
- Production of soft drinks and alcohol. Fresh cacao pulp juice, or sweatings, is collected, sterilised and

bottled. Alcoholic drinks, such as brandy, can be made by boiling the fresh juice, which is then cooled and fermented with yeast.

• Potash from cacao pod husk is used mainly for soft soap manufacture or as fertiliser for cacao, vegetables, and food crops. Fresh husks are spread out in the open to dry for one to two weeks. The dried husks are then incinerated in an ashing kiln.

• Pectin for jam and marmalade is extracted from the sweatings through a separate process.

• Cacao bean shells can be used as an organic mulch and soil conditioner for the garden.

• Cocoa butter is widely used in cosmetic products such as moisturising creams and soaps.

World Markets
and Tastes

Here are a few 'trivial' facts and figures which are quite revealing about people's chocolate eating habits:

- Three-quarters of the top consuming countries are European.
- The cocoa processing industry is dominated by three companies and some large-scale processing works, which process over 40% of the cacao beans produced in the world.
- The top ten chocolate manufacturers account for over 40% of global chocolate sales.
- 66% of chocolate is consumed between meals.
- 40% of the almonds grown and 20% of peanuts are used by chocolate manufacturers.
- 22% of chocolate is eaten between 8pm and midnight.
- More chocolate is eaten in winter than other seasons. No, really? Guilty as charged!

WORLD COCOA CONSUMPTION

Unsurprisingly, the major cocoa producing countries are not amongst the major consumers. Also unsurprisingly, the USA consumed over 32% of cocoa produced in 2005–6, although their near neighbours, Canada, only got through 2.5%. Germany came second with over 11%, France clocked up 10% and the UK, just over 9%. Russians ate or drank their way through nearly 8% and it surprised me to see that Japan consumed over 6%. Italy, home of many chocolatiers, consumed 5% and Spain, who were the world leaders in consumption for hundreds of years, now consume less than 4%. Two South American countries, Mexico and Brazil, each consumed around 3%, as did Poland. Belgium obviously goes for quality chocolate rather than quantity, with 2% of the cocoa produced.

WORLD CHOCOLATE CONSUMPTION

Global sales of chocolate have risen by about 20% in the last five years. The greatest markets are in Western Europe, where around 45% of chocolate confectionery is consumed; 20% is sold in the USA. Asian markets are still relatively untapped, but will no doubt be a target for development pretty soon.

DARK CHOCOLATE EATING

The dark chocolate market is estimated at between 5% and 10% of chocolate bars sold. Others are milk chocolate, white chocolate and filled bars. Most dark chocolate is eaten in Europe, where more than 10% of sales are in the form of tablets of chocolate.

On a recent stay in France I spent a bit of time looking at the range of chocolate available in even the smaller supermarkets. The range of dark chocolate available was phenomenal, with a huge choice in the percentage of cocoa butter, ranging from 35% to 99%. With prices in Euros competing very favourably with sterling, it's not surprising that a lot of our visitors bring home large quantities of tablets.

Of course, in the name of research, I had to try the 99%. The packaging blurb, thoughtfully included, complete with taste graphs and suggestions for enjoying the chocolate with other tastes, suggested building up to the experience with 70%, 86%, etc. first. The intensely bitter taste prevented anybody else trying to pinch a bit when I wasn't looking. Even I had to admit that a small amount of sugar would have enhanced the bitter, salty, dry feeling that was left. I used most for a chocolate and coffee mousse (see the recipe section). My best buy for cooking was a 70% cocoa butter version from the local Leclerc supermarket costing 39 centimes (about 25 pence) for 100g.

UK CHOCOLATE CONSUMPTION

In 2006, over £1 billion was spent on chocolate confectionery. Organic chocolate seems to be getting a bigger share of the market, with nearly £60 million in sales, although, overall, organic cocoa accounts for only 0.5% of total production. Fairtrade chocolate has a tiny share of the total. Less than 5% of all sales in Britain came from dark chocolate. Like the USA, UK residents seem to prefer their chocolate with milk and sugar. In the UK we eat about 10 kg per head per year. So who's eating most of mine? My husband doesn't eat any, so someone's eating rather a lot!

The UK market is dominated by three large international companies, Cadbury, Mars and Nestlé, who account for around 75 to 80% of sales in chocolate confectionery. The most popular chocolate Cadbury brands in 2003 were Cadbury's Dairy Milk, Crunchie and Cadbury's Buttons. Mars brands included Milky Way, M&Ms and Maltesers. Nestlé's best known brands were Kit Kat, Milky Bar and Yorkie.

CHOCOLATE CONSUMPTION IN OTHER COUNTRIES

Figures for various countries don't always seem to add up, or agree with each other. Maybe that's because of sensitivity between manufacturers or the sheer difficulty in defining how much chocolate there is in any

Country	Chocolate Consumption per head in Kg	Main producers
Belgium	11	Kraft, Mars Inc, Nestlé
China	0.1	
France	7	Nestlé, Kraft, Ferrero, Lindt
Germany	11	Ferrero, Mars, Kraft
Italy	4	Ferrero, Nestlé, Italian Spa, Mars
Japan	2	Meiji Seika Kaisha, Ezaki Glico, Morinaga & Co, Lotte
Russian Federation	2	Babaevsky, Krasny Oktyabr (Red October), Nestlé
Switzerland	11*	Lindt & Sprüngli, Nestlé, Kraft
UK	10	Cadbury, Mars, Nestlé
USA	6	Hershey Foods, Mars, Nestlé

*Figure possibly inflated by tourists buying to take home.

confectionery. The figures opposite are, therefore, only a guide. Perhaps unsurprisingly, the largest consumers in Europe seem to be in the north or in mountainous regions, where the winters are long and cold.

THE BIG COMPANIES
Processing and consumption of chocolate products are dominated by the West. 70% of the worldwide profit from chocolate sales is concentrated in these countries but not everyone gets to enjoy a share of the goodies. All but one of the top 20 countries that consume chocolate are considered economically well developed. Brazil is the only country on the list that considers chocolate to be a natural resource.

Six multi-national companies, including Nestlé, Mars and Cadbury, account for 80% of the world chocolate market. Europeans consume around 40% of the world's cocoa per year, 85% of which is imported from West Africa. Recent efforts to initiate a fair trade movement, encouraging the purchase of cacao from developing country producers at a fair price, have been slow to take off and tariffs continue to provide major problems, driving chocolate consumers and cocoa exporters further apart.

TRENDS IN CHOCOLATE CONSUMPTION
Chocolate consumption across markets has experienced some major changes, with the increasing appeal of organic, Fairtrade, single-origin, reduced sugar, dark and high cocoa-content chocolates. A recent survey in five European countries (Belgium, France, the United Kingdom, Germany and Switzerland) showed that single-origin chocolate is becoming more popular; 11% of those surveyed said they ate some Fairtrade chocolate. Fewer tried some organic chocolate and some sugar-free chocolate. Consumers, it seems, are demanding taste, convenience and products that address ethical and environmental concerns. The suggestion of chocolate having healthy properties also seems to have had an effect, or at least some varieties offering benefits, at the top end of the market.

ETHICAL BUYING

Recent changes in consumption have also had a significant impact on the demand for cacao beans. The increase in world cocoa demand during the past four years is partially explained by the improved image of chocolate as part of a healthy diet, resulting in increased purchases of labelled Fairtrade, organic and high liquor-quality cacao beans. The price premium received by some farmers over bulk cacao has surged since the second half of 2006.

Prices for cocoa powder have reached £600 to £675 per tonne while cocoa butter was worth around £2,200 per tonne. Farmers who had invested in cocoa niche markets are now starting to benefit. Demand for single-origin chocolate means that this area is the most dynamic and the fine or flavour, Fairtrade, organic and high-quality cacao beans are greatly in favour.

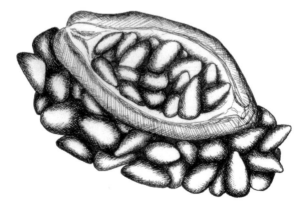

WORLD CONSUMPTION OF COCOA, 2004–5
World average, per head = 0.57 kg

European average	2.027 kg
Italy	1.9 kg
Spain	2.1 kg
Sweden	2.13 kg
Netherlands	2.14 kg
Germany	3.4 kg
UK	3.6 kg
Norway	3.8 kg
France	4 kg
Switzerland	5.1 kg
African average	0.15 kg
America	2.6 kg
Asia	0.123 kg
Australasia	2.6 kg

ESTIMATED SHARE OF DARK CHOCOLATE TABLETS IN 2006

MORE THAN 20%	BETWEEN 10% AND 20%	LESS THAN 10%
Austria	Denmark	Denmark
Belgium	Germany	Ireland
Finland	Greece	United Kingdom
France	Norway	United States
Italy	Sweden	
Netherlands		
Portugal		
Spain		
Switzerland		

THE TOP TEN COMPANIES

COMPANY	TOTAL SALES IN 2005 (IN US$ MILLIONS)
Mars Inc.	9,546
Cadbury Schweppes PLC	8,126
Nestlé SA	7,973
Ferrero SpA	5,580
Hershey Foods Corp.	4,881
Kraft Foods Inc.	2,250
Meiji Seika Kaisha Ltd	1,693
Lindt & Sprüngli	1,673
Barry Callebaut AG	1,427
Ezaki Glico Co.	1,239

Health and Nutrition

Cocoa is a natural food which contains many nutritional properties, including carbohydrates, fats, proteins, minerals and vitamins. It is said to contain around 300 compounds altogether. As a source of energy chocolate is a popular, handy, portable form of carbohydrate. Milk chocolate contains about 500 calories per 100 g. That's where the problems begin. The good news about chocolate is that the darker varieties contain a lot of good things and don't have all the fat and extra sugar that milk chocolate contains.

Like many other natural foods, such as fruit, nuts and vegetables, and drinks like tea and red wine, cocoa contains a group of chemicals that can produce health benefits for a range of conditions, although many of these benefits may be lost during processing. The quantities of chocolate liquor in the chocolate will also have an effect — the greater the amount of liquor, the greater are the possible effects.

Unlike other natural foods, cacao undergoes many changes during processing, so the following information is only meant to be a loose guide. The huge variety of types of cocoa and chocolate will all have different make-ups, so you can't rely on the content of some compounds acting in a particular way.

Per 100 g cacao seed there is approximately:

> 3.6 g water
> 12 g protein
> 46 g fat
> 34.7 g carbohydrate
> 8.6 g fibre
> 3.4 g ash
> 106 mg calcium
> 537 mg phosphorous
> 3.6 mg iron

Since 2003 cocoa solids and milk solids have been declared on labels.

Example of milk chocolate and dark chocolate recipes:

RECIPE (in grams)	MILK CHOCOLATE	DARK CHOCOLATE
Cocoa liquor	12 g	57 g
Added cocoa butter	15 g	2 g
CBE	3 g	3 g
Whole milk powder	20 g	0
Sugar	49.5 g	37.5 g
Lecithin	0.5 g	0.5 g
Total	100 g	100 g
Cacao beans	35 g	75 g

Other sources give the following major components of manufactured chocolate as approximately:

- cocoa butter   54%
- protein   11.5%
- cellulose   9%
- tannic acids and colour 6%
- water   5%
- salts   2.6%
- natural sugars   1%
- caffeine   0.2%
- organic acids and aromas 10%

The amount of cocoa mass will range from 7% to 15% in milk chocolate and 30% to 70% in dark chocolate. Although, as mentioned before, 99% cocoa chocolate is also available if you are feeling adventurous. This doesn't give a particularly helpful picture. Some of the creamy, dreamy varieties currently being advertised might appear to be solid chocolate, but are not. Reading the label won't give you enough information to know that the bar contains 45% sugar and around 30% fat. Of the quarter that is made from cocoa, four-fifths is cocoa butter.

Interestingly, a third of all chocolate bars launched in 2006 were dark chocolate products. Even the milk chocolate producers are starting to branch into the 'healthier' chocolate areas.

In raw seeds there are also said to be traces of thiamine, riboflavin and pyridoxine, and slightly more than traces of nicotinamide (niacin) and pantothenic acid.

The fatty acids of cocoa butter contain about a quarter palmitic acid, about a third stearic acids and a similar amount of oleic acid. The fat in dark chocolate is, therefore, mostly a saturated vegetable fat like olive oil, that doesn't clog arteries.

That's the good news. The not so good news is that figures can vary, depending on the type of cocoa variety and the processing it has undergone. Fermented beans also contain different chemical compounds from unfermented ones. Unfermented beans contain caffeic acid and also vanillic acid, still present in fermented beans.

Although cocoa contains only small amounts of some minerals and vitamins, these are, nevertheless, essential to the body, so eating chocolate (in moderation, of course) probably does have some effect. By the time the cocoa becomes chocolate the likelihood of these compounds having a significant effect is questionable, but we can always hope as we chomp. Anyway, the best way to go about our recommended daily intake of this and that is to eat a mixed diet, which can include some chocolate and cocoa.

There's also the undeniable feel-good factor with chocolate and the sense of giving yourself a treat. Advertisers spend millions of pounds every year persuading us of this fact, while playing down the effect of over indulgence on the calorie front.

LABELLING FOR AVOIDANCE OF FOODSTUFFS AND DIETARY REQUIREMENTS

Some of the larger chocolate manufacturers give detailed lists of ingredients on their websites, so that those with dietary requirements or who need to avoid certain foods, can check whether a product is safe, but not all manufacturers seem to do this. For instance, Cadbury and Nestlé both give nutrition data by product so that you can see which may have nuts, egg, wheat, etc. The reading of labels has become a pretty routine procedure for some of us, who have to watch sugars, fats, etc., but it must be a nightmare for coeliac or non-gluten eaters. Vegetarians also need to watch out, as some brands contain animal fats, whey and emulsifiers. A recent change in the recipe for one major national producer's famous product created quite a furore.

Some manufacturers provide the percentage of chocolate in a finished chocolate confection as a label quoting percentage of cocoa. This refers to the combined percentage of both cocoa solids and cocoa butter in the bar, not just the percentage of cocoa solids.

VITAMINS, MINERALS
AND OTHER BENEFICIAL COMPOUNDS THAT MAY BE PRESENT IN COCOA OR CHOCOLATE

CAFFEIC ACID

This is not the same as caffeine and is present in unfermented cacao beans. It is a naturally occurring phenolic compound, which is found in many other fruits, vegetables and herbs, including coffee. Caffeic acid has been shown to act as a carcinogenic inhibitor. It is also known as an antioxidant and anti-inflammatory agent.

CAFFEINE

This is present in small amounts. Forastero beans contain less than criollos (1.4 to 1.7%). This means that a 175 ml (6 oz) cup of cocoa may contain 13 mg of caffeine. A similar-sized cup of tea may contain 10 to 50 mg and expresso coffee 310 mg. A shot of cola will contain between 10 and 25 mg, depending on the brand. See below for theobromine.

COPPER

Cacao beans contain very high levels of copper. Most of the mineral remains preserved after the beans are processed into cocoa or chocolate. Copper is a basic mineral necessary for nutrition and normal development. It builds and maintains red blood cells. While low copper can lead to fragile blood vessels, high copper levels are much more common and too much copper inhibits the action of some flavonoids. Dark chocolate has not only the highest epicatechin (see below) flavonoid content, but also the highest copper level. Light or milk chocolate has the lowest copper level and also the lowest flavonoid content.

CALCIUM

Present in milk chocolate. Both magnesium and calcium are needed for healthy bones. Calcium is essential for the normal growth and maintenance of bones and teeth. Requirements must be met throughout life, with long-term calcium deficiency leading to an increasing occurrence of osteoporosis, particularly amongst women over 50, where bones deteriorate and there is an increased risk of fractures.

EPICATECHIN

Epicatechin is a flavonoid (see below) that improves blood flow and cardiac health. Cocoa contains relatively high amounts of epicatechin and has been found to have nearly twice the antioxidant content of red wine and maybe three times that of green tea, although the beneficial effects are minimal, as the antioxidants are rapidly lost from the body. Research into epicatechins is big business and there are calls for it to be renamed as a vitamin.

FATTY ACIDS

COCOA BUTTER contains palmitic acid. This is one of the most common saturated fatty acids found in animals and plants. It is a major component of the oil from palm trees. Butter, cheese, milk and meat also contain this fatty acid.

STEARIC ACID is a waxy solid, used along with simple sugar or corn syrup as a hardener in confectionery. Stearic acid is also an ingredient in making candles, soaps, plastics, oil pastels and cosmetics, and for softening rubber.

OLEIC ACID is a monounsaturated omega-9 fatty acid found in animal and vegetable sources, also present in cocoa butter.

FLAVONOIDS

Some of the beneficial compounds identified in cocoa are called flavonoids and are most commonly known for activity as antioxidants. They are sometimes referred to as bioflavonoids, because they are biological in origin. Interest has grown in them for their medicinal potential in preventing cancers and heart disease. They seem to work by modifying bodily reactions to viruses, allergens and cancer-producing agents, showing anti-microbial, anti-inflammatory and anti-cancer activity. Other foods high in flavonoids include tea, red wine and broccoli. Flavonoids on their own are of little direct antioxidant value and are not absorbed well by the body, but it is thought that they work by increasing uric acid levels. The body treats them as foreign compounds which it wants to get rid of as quickly as it can. At the same time it gets rid of other unwanted compounds and increases the antioxidant capacity of the blood.

Flavanols are a subclass of flavonoids. They are powerful antioxidants and cacao beans are a good source of flavanols.

IRON
Iron is found in every cell in the body. Iron links with protein to form haemoglobin, which is the oxygen transporter in your blood. Iron keeps your immune system healthy and helps to produce energy. Insufficient iron leads to anaemia.

MAGNESIUM
Helps to regulate the nerve and muscle tone. Magnesium keeps the muscles relaxed by preventing calcium entering the nerve cells. Insufficient magnesium may lead to muscle spasms or cramps, migraine, high blood pressure and fatigue. Some research with rats used a cocoa-derived product, used in some European countries as a dietary complement added to milk, to aid recovery from chronic magnesium deficiency.

MANGANESE
Manganese is an essential mineral trace element. Its name comes from the Greek word for magic. Manganese is an antioxidant that is important in the breakdown of amino acids and the production of energy. It activates various enzymes which are important for proper digestion of foods. It helps break down cholesterol and feeds the nerves and brain. It is necessary for normal skeletal development, maintaining sex hormone production and for regulating blood sugar levels.

PHENYLETHYLAMINE
Phenylethylamine (PEA) increases attention and activity in animals and has been said to have relieved depression in 60% of human patients suffering from the illness. It has been suggested that PEA deficiency may be the cause of a common form of depressive illness. PEA is a stimulant, found in chocolate and also in the brain. A tiny amount of PEA is released at moments of emotional euphoria, raising

blood pressure and heart rate, but there is little to prove that PEA found in foods increases PEA in the brain. Cheddar cheese, salami and pickled herring all contain more PEA than chocolate.

PHOSPHORUS

Phosphorus is a mineral that makes up 1% of the total body weight. It is present in every cell of the body, but 85% of the body's phosphorus is found in the bones and teeth. It plays an important role in the body's use of carbohydrates and fats and in the synthesis of protein for the growth, maintenance and repair of cells and tissues. It is also crucial for the production of a molecule the body uses to store energy. Phosphorus works with the B vitamins. It assists in the contraction of muscles, in kidney function, in maintaining the regularity of the heartbeat, and in nerve conduction. The main food sources are the protein food groups of meat and milk but there are small quantities in green vegetables. A meal plan that provides adequate amounts of calcium and protein also provides an adequate amount of phosphorus.

POTASSIUM

Potassium helps to contract all the muscles in the body. It is essential for heart function and maintaining normal blood pressure. Studies have shown that potassium reduces blood pressure and the risk of strokes.

SELENIUM

Selenium is present as a trace element. It may help prevent cancer by acting as an antioxidant.

SODIUM

Sodium is an element that the body needs to function properly and occurs naturally in most foods. The body uses sodium to regulate blood pressure and blood volume. Sodium is also critical for the functioning of muscles and nerves. Drinking water also contains sodium, although the amount varies depending on the source.

THEOBROMINE

Theobromine belongs to a class of alkaloid molecules that occur naturally in as many as 60 different plant species and include caffeine. Different types of chocolate contain varying amounts of theobromine, with dark chocolate having two to five times as much as milk chocolate, and high quality chocolate containing more than low quality chocolate. Cocoa beans themselves contain extremely variable amounts of theobromine. The effects on humans is as a mild stimulant, similar to caffeine, but on a much smaller scale. It is mildly diuretic and relaxes the smooth muscles of the bronchi in the lungs.

Levels of theobromine in humans are halved between 6 to 10 hours after consumption. Theobromine has quite a different effect on animals, who can keep theobromine in their bloodstreams for up to 20 hours. Cocoa and chocolate products may be toxic or lethal to cats, dogs and other domestic animals such as horses. The animal's heart, central nervous system and kidneys may be affected. Early signs of theobromine poisoning in dogs include nausea and vomiting, restlessness, diarrhoea, muscle tremors and incontinence. More advanced symptoms involve cardiac problems, internal bleeding and seizures. It's best to eat the chocolate yourself and not to give the dog a treat!

VITAMIN A
Vitamin A is a group of compounds that play an important role in vision, bone growth, reproduction and cell growth. It helps to regulate the immune system, preventing or fighting off infections by making white blood cells that destroy harmful bacteria and viruses. Vitamin A promotes healthy surface linings to the eyes, respiratory, urinary and intestinal tracts. When those linings break down, it becomes easier for bacteria to enter the body and cause infection. Vitamin A also helps the skin and mucous membranes function as a barrier to bacteria and viruses.

In cocoa butter, palmitate is an antioxidant and a vitamin. It is a compound added to low-fat milk to replace the vitamin content lost through the removal of milk fat.

VITAMIN B1 THIAMIN
Thiamin helps the body to metabolise carbohydrates and fat to produce energy. It is essential for normal growth

and development, and helps maintain proper functioning of the heart and the nervous and digestive systems. Thiamine cannot be stored in the body. Once absorbed, the vitamin is concentrated in muscle tissue.

VITAMIN B3 NIACIN
Niacin helps the body turn the food we eat into energy. It also helps keep the nervous and digestive systems healthy and synthesise fatty acids, cholesterol and steroids. *NICOTINIC ACID*, a form of niacin, is used in pharmacology.

VITAMIN B2 RIBOFLAVIN
This is present in milk chocolate and cocoa. It is necessary in the release of energy from carbohydrates, the activation of many vitamins, and the breakdown of fat. It is also needed for growth and tissue repair, and the synthesis of red blood cells.

VITAMIN B5 PANTOTHENIC ACID
Pantothenic acid is a water-soluble vitamin and essential nutrient, required to sustain life. It is critical in the metabolism and synthesis of carbohydrates, proteins and fats.

VITAMIN B6 PYRIDOXINE
Allows the body to use and store energy from carbohydrates and protein, as well as helping to form haemoglobin.

VITAMIN E
Vitamin E is the body's main fat-soluble antioxidant. It plays a big role in preventing cardiovascular disease and is one of the main antioxidants found in cholesterol. It helps prevent free radicals that would damage the cell membranes by oxidising the cholesterol. If cholesterol is oxidised it causes problems by sticking to blood vessel walls and blocking arteries.

ZINC
Zinc is second only to iron in its concentration in the body. The body needs zinc for the immune system to work properly. It plays a role in cell division, cell growth, wound healing, and the breakdown of carbohydrates. Zinc

is also needed for the senses of smell and taste. Most zinc is consumed through high protein foods such as meat and fish. Low protein diets and vegetarian diets tend to be low in zinc.

POSSIBLE HEALTH BENEFITS
FROM CONSUMING COCOA AND CHOCOLATE

This section attempts to give a balanced view of the research and current ideas on the positive and negative effects associated with eating chocolate. You need to decide for yourself how you feel. As always, the information on conditions mentioned is of a general interest level and should not be substituted for medical advice from qualified professionals.

Growing awareness amongst consumers and their buying power might even bring changes to the processing of cocoa, so that more of the beneficial compounds remain unspoiled. The variety and price of a bewildering array of products, along with media pressure, could start to bring about more changes. Until then, the advice seems to be to read labels carefully and to avoid milk chocolate if there is a concern about health. Another thing I've discovered is that the most expensive brands are not always the healthiest!

Stories on the health benefits of consuming cocoa products increasingly make the headlines. Just how much of the research has been funded by the manufacturers or multinational corporations is a different matter. Following the discovery that chocolate is a good source of epicatechins, or polyphenols of the flavonoid group, research appears to have found that they protect against heart disease, cancer and various other medical conditions. If you can justify the view that there is some benefit to be gained from eating chocolate, you can feel less guilty about eating it.

Some of the claims are that chocolate:

- reduces the risk of heart disease
- reduces the risk of some cancers
- releases endorphins in the brain, which act as pain-relievers
- may reduce stress and have a calming effect
- may make you live longer

Not all of these findings have been reported to the same extent, or particularly widely. Another problem is the difference between consuming pure cocoa and one or more of the many processed chocolate products. Most people go for the latter, with the associated sugar, corn syrup, milk fats, etc., where the cocoa content may be less than 20%.

COCOA AND HEART DISEASE

Research funded by a chocolate manufacturing giant over the past 15 years seems to suggest that consuming cocoa which is rich in flavanols may affect the nitric oxide produced in the lining of the blood vessels. Nitric oxide signals the surrounding smooth muscles to relax, which dilates the arteries to increase blood flow. It also prevents platelets from sticking to artery walls. This effect means that nitric oxide may be responsible for the possible beneficial effects of cocoa on blood pressure.

Everyone needs this gas to carry out key processes. For bodybuilders, nitric oxide supplements may prove useful in increasing growth by increasing blood flow to certain areas of the body. Signs of deficiency include physical weakness and extreme fatigue.

Researchers in the USA have conducted studies that suggest flavanol-rich cocoa drinks being consumed by healthy people can inhibit platelet activity and increase the time it takes for blood to clot. This could be important in preventing thrombosis and blocked arteries. The research suggested that the effects were the same as taking a low dose of aspirin regularly; 25 g (1 oz) of semi-sweet chocolate pieces appeared to have the same effect on a group of 20- to 40-year-olds as 80 mg of aspirin. This is not a call to give up medication in favour of chocolate! The effects of aspirin last longer than flavanols in chocolate.

It seems also that cocoa flavanols may benefit cardiovascular conditions by reducing inflammation of blood vessels. There is evidence that flavanols are antioxidants which help to resist damage to cells by free radicals. Free radicals are atoms or molecules that have lost an electron. They roam the body in search of their missing part. The way to get it back is to combine with oxygen, but when they do this they create another free radical from the molecule they took the electron from. This begins a chain reaction which can cause the number of free radicals in the body to increase to a dangerous level.

A study of the difference on blood pressure between two groups of people from Central America proved interesting. The island-dwelling people of Kuna had a low tendency towards age-related high blood pressure, as well as low levels of heart disease, cancer, stroke and diabetes. People from Kuna who migrated to Panama did develop high blood pressure. Further study showed that the people who stayed on Kuna ate and drank large quantities of flavanol-rich cocoa, up to 40 cups per week, without the associated quantities of fats and sugars of milk chocolate, of course. Flavanols, like epicatechin, have tended to be removed from commercial cocoas because they have a bitter taste.

Another study in Italy compared healthy people eating 100 g of dark chocolate a day with those eating 100 g of white chocolate a day. After 15 days the blood pressure of the dark chocolate group was significantly lower.

Studies have also shown that stearic acid, one of the main fatty acids in cocoa butter, does not raise blood pressure. So, maybe if we keep to the dark chocolate, we can still enjoy some now and again. Foods rich in cocoa appear to reduce blood pressure. There is now a suggestion that drinking green and black tea may not, as previously thought, have as great an effect as drinking cocoa.

ANTIOXIDANTS
Scientific research into flavonoids is finding similar results with compounds in fruits and vegetables, tea, red wine and tomatoes. The tea, grape and chocolate industries are some of the groups exploring antioxidants' potential benefits. Until recently tea was thought to contain the largest amount of antioxidants, but new research indicates that dark chocolate has four times as much as tea. Researchers in one test found that dark chocolate had 53.5 mg of catechins per 100 g, whereas milk chocolate contained 15.9 mg per 100 g, and black tea contained 13.9 mg per 100 ml. The exact make-up of the chocolate used is, however, unknown.

Studies show that cocoa powder, dark chocolate and milk chocolate have higher Oxygen Radical Absorption Capacity (ORAC) values than many common foods, such as prunes and blueberries. An antioxidant is a substance that inhibits oxidation or reactions from free radicals. The process of oxidation can damage cells, leading to conditions like cataracts, heart disease and even cancer.

The main antioxidants in chocolate seem to be the flavonoids, catechin and epicatechin. Epicatechin seems to have an effect on the oxidation rate of LDL or bad cholesterol, which can build up in blood vessels and lead to atherosclerosis. This is a major cause of heart disease.

The effects of these flavonoids have been studied in the USA. Studies compared the effects of consuming high-flavonoid and low-flavonoid chocolate. Another study in Australia showed that the consumption of both high-flavonoid and low-flavonoid chocolate was associated with reduced free radical levels, so maybe there is another factor to consider. Research can be confusing, or maybe the chocolate used in the test makes a difference. Maybe there is scope for companies to develop epicatechin supplements or capsules.

TEA, RED WINE OR A NICE CUP OF COCOA?
Research into the consumption of drinks to promote health came up with some interesting results. Cocoa led other drinks because of its high content of flavonoids.

Phenolic compounds protect plants against insects and pathogens, and they remain active even after food processing. Eating chocolate bars instead of drinking cocoa may not have the same effect, because chocolate contains saturated fats. Cocoa has about 0.33 g of fat per standard serving, compared with 8 g of fat in a standard-size, 40 g chocolate bar.

Faced with the prospect of drinking red wine, green tea or cocoa, the suggestion seems obvious: drink all three, but not at the same time of day.

CHOCOLATE AS AN ANTI-INFLAMMATORY

Inflammation is present in chronic conditions like arthritis and has even been associated with the development of some forms of cancer. The process of inflammation seems to involve increased levels of leukotriene in the body. A study in Germany showed that the epicatechin in chocolate helps decrease levels of leukotriene, so eating chocolate may help reduce inflammation by reducing leukotriene.

CHOCOLATE REDUCING THE RISK OF CANCER?

There is a suggestion that cocoa and chocolate may be able to contribute to reducing the risk of certain types of cancer. Research has shown that some carcinogenic processes are inhibited by antioxidants, such as those found in cocoa and chocolate. That isn't exactly news anymore, but the claim that chocolate-eating may, alongside the regular intake of food containing other antioxidants, such as vegetables, fruit, tea or soy products, lower the incidence of various types of cancer, seems like good news. The intake of antioxidants, including those from cocoa and chocolate, seems to inhibit several phases of the processes leading to cancer.

CHOCOLATE FOR LONG LIFE?

Chocolate consumption has been linked to longer life. A survey of healthy 65-year-old men in the USA revealed that those who ate sweets containing chocolate reportedly lived longer. Mind you, healthy people tend to live longer anyway . . . Mortality was lowest among those eating chocolate up to three times a month and slightly higher among those who indulged three or more times a week. Those who ate none at all had the highest mortality of all. I wonder what their vice was?

ACNE

Consumption of chocolate has always been said to be a cause of acne. Pure chocolate contains antioxidants which aid better skin complexion. Experiments in the USA fed subjects chocolate or a bar with similar amounts of fat, sugar, etc. It was found that consumption of chocolate, frequent or not, had no effect on the development of acne. Although pure chocolate can aid skin conditions and complexion, chocolate bars with milk content may contribute to acne. It is not the chocolate itself that causes acne, but the milk and sugar with which the chocolate is mixed.

COUGHS

It appears from UK research that a cocoa compound may be effective at preventing persistent coughing. Theobromine was found to be more effective than traditional remedies like codeine. Coughs lasting several weeks after a viral infection showed improvement. It may be that lung disease patients may eventually benefit from the research. In addition, there are no side effects as there are with codeine, which causes drowsiness and constipation. More work is being carried out. Chocolate appears to soothe and moisten the throat, and researchers believe that theobromine acts on the sensory nerve endings of the vagus nerve, running through the airways in the lungs to the brain.

I always wondered why a piece of chocolate appeared to soothe the throat as it melted.

DIARRHOEA

South American and some European cultures have apparently used cocoa to treat diarrhoea for hundreds of years. Studies in Germany and the USA have shown that flavonoids can inhibit the development of fluids resulting in diarrhoea.

PAIN RELIEF

Chocolate is said to be a natural analgesic. High fat chocolate foods trigger the brain's production of natural opiates.

CHOCOLATE AS A MOOD ENHANCER

Like sugar and other sweet food, chocolate stimulates the release of natural body hormones called endorphins that generate feelings of pleasure and well-being.

Chocolate contains a variety of substances that may have an effect on body chemistry. These include:

- Anandamide, a neurotransmitter. This is broken down quickly after it has been produced. Other chemicals in chocolate may inhibit the natural breakdown of anandamide. This means that anandamide may stick around longer, making us feel good longer, when we eat chocolate.
- Tryptophan, an amino acid that is a compound enabling serotonin to work. Serotonin is believed to play an important role in the regulation of moods, pleasure, body temperature and sleep, amongst other things.
- Phenyethylamine can cause endorphin releases in the brain. However, unlike its synthetic derivative amphetamine, it is quickly metabolised and prevented from reaching the brain in significant concentrations.
- Caffeine. This stimulant is present mainly in coffee and tea, but exists in chocolate in very small amounts.
- Theobromine, the major methylxanthine in cocoa and chocolate.

People who are unhappy, stressed or otherwise emotionally upset have been turning to chocolate for hundreds of years to help them feel better. One UK study has shown an association between eating chocolate and the improvement of mood. Both chocolate and a non-chocolate, caffeine and theobromine combination were used, suggesting that caffeine and theobromine are at least contributing to this effect.

Theobromine is just one of the causes of chocolate's mood-elevating effects. This mild stimulant belongs to the methylxanthine family, which also includes the similar compound caffeine. Most people who love chocolate enjoy the unique taste and feeling of it melting in the mouth. Some of the pleasure of eating chocolate is due to the fact that its melting point is slightly below human body temperature. Chocolate intake has been linked with release of serotonin in the brain, which produces feelings of pleasure. Chocoholics who were given cocoa in capsules, without the added fat and sugar of creamy chocolate and without the feel of chocolate melting in their mouths, gained no benefit and claimed it had no satisfying effect at all.

One study apparently indicated that melting chocolate in your mouth produced an increase in brain activity and heart rate that was more intense than that associated with passionate kissing. It also lasted four times as long after the activity had ended. That may or may not have come from research funded by a chocolate manufacturer. Maybe we should all try our own personal research!

Most scientists are sceptical that chocolate can produce mood-altering effects. Chemicals like tryptophan and phenylethylamine, which are also found in many other foodstuffs, are present in chocolate only in very small quantities. That doesn't appear to have stopped advertisers selling the idea of chocolate and love in the same breath.

MILD EFFECTS
There are unlikely to be sufficient levels of the chemicals in chocolate to have the effects associated with pharmaceutical doses of the same chemicals. These compounds cause physiological actions ranging from stimulation of the central nervous system to stimulation of the cardiac muscle and relaxation of other muscles.

Compounds like caffeine have effects on behaviour, mood and physical performance. Caffeine is present in relatively low amounts compared with coffee. Most chocolate contains too little of this compound for a reasonable serving to create effects in humans that are on a par with a caffeine buzz.

Current research suggests that the weak stimulant effect of chocolate is due mainly to theobromine. You would need to eat around a dozen chocolate bars to get the same amount of caffeine as one cup of coffee. I'll stick to the coffee to keep me going.

GUILTY CHOCOLATE EATING

Mood and intake of chocolate was investigated in 40 women: 20 chocolate 'addicts' and 20 'controls' noted hunger, mood, intensity of craving and amount of chocolate eaten, in a diary for a week. The 'addicts' reported a much greater number of eating episodes (surprise, surprise) and consumed a larger amount of chocolate than the other group. Depression, guilt and craving were rated higher and feeling contented or relaxed as lower before eating than in the control group. Feelings of guilt, however, in eating chocolate increased in the 'addicts' and they didn't get any benefit from feelings of depression, so eating chocolate didn't enhance their mood.

The downside of eating chocolate to make yourself feel better, apart from the guilt, is that when the effects of the chocolate wear off, blood pressure and blood sugar will lower and be followed by a drop in energy that leaves you more tired than before you ate the chocolate in the first place.

COGNITIVE FUNCTION

Theobromine increases alertness and does not have the same effect on the heart as caffeine. Cocoa and chocolate have been reported to enhance mental activity. A study measured the ability to think and process information. This function apparently improved after the consumption of chocolate. Both milk and dark chocolate had this effect, but white chocolate did not.

Methylxanthine, which is not present in white chocolate, may be the contributor here.

The phenylethylamine found in chocolate is related to amphetamines, which are strong stimulants. These increase the activity of neurotransmitters (brain chemicals) in parts of the brain that control our ability to pay attention and stay alert.

It is interesting to note that chocolate is a very potent stimulant for horses and its use is banned in horse-racing. This is probably just as well, given the knowledge that chocolate is toxic to many animals, including horses.

ADDICTIONS

Addiction is associated with the formation and reinforcement of unusual neurotransmitter pathways in the brain. Maybe every time a chocoholic eats chocolate, the brain is gradually being rewired to make the craving greater. Most modern commercial chocolate products contain substantial amounts of sugar. This fact alone may partly explain chocolate's addictive properties.

Anandamide is a neurotransmitter that targets the same brain structures as the active ingredient in cannabis. To make a substantial impact on the brain's own natural anandamide levels, experts estimate you would need to eat several kilos of chocolate.

Findings from California suggest that chocolate contains active substances that have the same effect on the brain as marijuana, and that these chemicals may be responsible for certain drug-induced psychoses associated with chocolate craving.

Chocolate is widely believed to enhance the effect of marijuana. A practical implication is that the amount of marijuana needed for medicinal purposes, say, may be decreased by using it with chocolate: reducing both the risks and cost associated with marijuana. It has been calculated that an adult would have to eat around 25 lb of chocolate all at once to get a marijuana-like effect. That's about the average yearly consumption in one go!

Other research has shown that heroin addicts tend to have an increased liking for chocolate, possibly because it triggers the brain to release dopamine, a neurotransmitter.

PMS AND SAD
Premenstrual syndrome (PMS) and seasonal affective disorder (SAD) are frequently associated with lethargy and increased appetite, particularly with a preference for carbohydrates, including chocolate. Central serotonin pathways modulate eating patterns. It has been suggested that the excessive carbohydrate intake by patients with PMS and SAD temporarily relieves the symptoms via an increased central serotonergic activity.

Another suggestion as to why many women report particular chocolate cravings when premenstrual is that chocolate contains magnesium. A shortage of magnesium can exacerbate premenstrual tension. Cravings during pregnancy could indicate mild anaemia, or a need for more iron. There are better ways to get more iron in pregnancy than chocolate eating, though.

APHRODISIAC?
Although the Aztec king Montezuma had a reputation for being a bit of a goer, and people have assumed that chocolate has a strong aphrodisiac quality, there is little substance to this claim. However, high levels of serotonin can produce feelings of elation. High levels of Phenylethylamine help promote feelings of attraction, excitement and apprehension. Phenylethylamine works by stimulating the brain's pleasure centres and reaches peak levels during orgasm. That might take an awful lot of chocolate!

IN THE MOOD
The reputed aphrodisiac qualities of chocolate are most often associated with the sensual pleasure of its consumption. Suggestion has been made that serotonin and phenylethylamine can act as mild sexual stimulants.

ERECTILE DYSFUNCTION
One of the main physiological causes of impotence, or erectile dysfunction, is inability of the blood vessels in

the penis to dilate enough to allow blood flow and engorgement. The most important chemical involved in this process is nitric oxide.

Effects include blood vessel dilation, neurotransmission and penile erections. Viagra stimulates erections primarily by enhancing signalling through nitric oxide to the penis. Herbal supplements that can help dilate blood vessels include ginseng.

ME/CHRONIC FATIGUE SYNDROME
A recent study by UK researchers has also found that dark chocolate may help reduce the symptoms of chronic fatigue syndrome, also known as ME.

POSSIBLE NEGATIVE EFFECTS OF CHOCOLATE ON HEALTH

OBESITY
Obesity occurs when calorific intake exceeds energy output. It results from excess body fat which is stored when not required for energy. Obesity is not caused by any one food, but by overeating high energy foods without appropriate use of energy to burn the calories. Consumption of sugar is a well-known cause. It contributes to or aggravates a host of medical conditions.

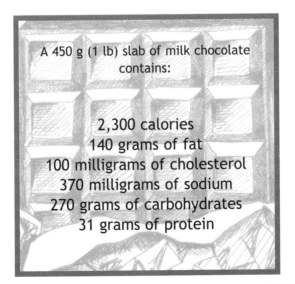

A 450 g (1 lb) slab of milk chocolate contains:

2,300 calories
140 grams of fat
100 milligrams of cholesterol
370 milligrams of sodium
270 grams of carbohydrates
31 grams of protein

	100 GRAMS OF CHOCOLATE WILL CONTAIN APPROXIMATELY:			
CHOCOLATE	TOTAL FAT	CALORIES	PROTEIN	CARBS
Milk	530	7.8	57	30
Dark, semi-sweet	495	4	61	26
Milk with wholenuts	540	9	44	36
Sugar-coated chocolate drops	497	5.3	69	22
Milk, fruit and nut	480	7.8	54	26

THE RECOMMENDED DAILY CALORIE INTAKE FOR ADULTS IN THE UK IS:

Men   2,550
Women   1,940

Manufacturers are now marketing smaller versions, for example offering less than 99 calories per bar, but that only accounts for 17.5 g of product.

A lot of the chocolate consumed is in the form of chocolate biscuit or filled chocolate coatings. These contain far less chocolate but potentially much more fat and sugar.

So you can see where the problems begin. Add to that a lack of exercise and there's no surprise that obesity is a significant risk factor in this country, where we each eat, on average, 10 kg of the stuff per year. Levels of obesity have tripled in England since 1980. Currently, over half of all women, and about two-thirds of men, are either overweight or obese. Obesity amongst children and young people is even more worrying. Being overweight increases the risk of developing heart disease, Type 2 diabetes, high blood pressure and osteoarthritis. Obesity has been attributed to about 18 million sick days and 30,000 deaths a year in England. Widespread obesity is draining NHS resources and a report recently concluded that a dramatic increase in funding will be required to tackle health problems such as obesity. Well, I'm glad I've got all that off my chest!

CARDIOVASCULAR DISEASE
Despite the benefits that have been discovered from eating dark chocolate and drinking good quality cocoa, this doesn't mean that you can consume large quantities of dark chocolate in an attempt to protect against cardiovascular disease. Remember that the fats and sugar level are also factors in heart disease. Cocoa butter in chocolate contains saturated fat, which can increase blood cholesterol levels, and high cholesterol may contribute to heart disease.

CANCER RISK
Several population studies have observed an increase in the risk of some cancers among people who frequently consume quantities of sweet foods such as milk chocolate.

DIABETES
People with diabetes should base their diet around starchy carbohydrate foods such as potatoes, pasta, bread and plenty of fresh fruit and vegetables. There are no banned foods, but cakes, sweets and chocolate need to be enjoyed in moderation, preferably at the end of a meal. Before I was diagnosed with Type 2 diabetes a couple of years ago I had to have a daily fix of a couple of squares of chocolate, especially in winter, or at the end of a day teaching. Now I indulge in the dark varieties and feel I appreciate the flavour of the chocolate more when it isn't covered with extra sugar and milk. Cooking with chocolate has become a whole new delight. See the recipe section!

A campaign encouraging people to measure their waists to see if they are at risk of diabetes suggests that waist measurements of 94 cm (37 inches) or more for men, or 89 cm (35 inches) for those of South Asian origin, and 79 cm (31.5 inches) or more for all women constituted a risk.

Eating sugar or chocolate does not cause diabetes, which can be caused by a combination of genetic and environmental factors. Eating a diet high in fat and sugar can cause you to become overweight and being overweight increases your risk of developing Type 2 diabetes. A healthy diet and regular exercise are recommended to control your weight.

TOOTH DECAY

This is a tricky one to place, given some of the research going on. I came down on the side of possible negative effects, although some would argue for its positive effects.

Some researchers believe that the effects of eating chocolate on tooth decay are either overstated or entirely false. However, to say that something is less harmful doesn't really mean that it is healthy. They say that chocolate has not been proven to cause cavities or tooth decay but helps thwart mouth bacteria.

Tooth cavities start when bacteria produce a sticky molecule called glucan. This helps the bacteria anchor themselves to teeth and form plaque. These and other bacteria in plaque convert sugar to acids, which eat away at the surface of the tooth and lead to cavities.

Many dental research studies suggest that chocolate may be less apt to promote tooth decay than had traditionally been believed and that chocolate does not contain any more sugar than other foods, but this doesn't seem much of an argument somehow. However, a study showed that certain chocolate products tested were found to be among the snack foods contributing least to tooth decay. The protein, calcium and phosphate in milk chocolate may provide protective effects on tooth enamel. Another point in its favour is that because of the natural fat content and its tendency to melt in the mouth, chocolate clears the mouth relatively faster than other confections. The time fermentable carbohydrate remains in contact with tooth surfaces has a bearing on the potential to produce cavities.

Researchers in Japan have suggested that some components of chocolate may be added to toothpaste and mouthwash. Cocoa bean husk, which usually goes to waste in the production of chocolate, is a good source of these components.

INDIGESTION
Theobromine is also a contributing factor in acid reflux because it relaxes the oesophageal sphincter muscle, allowing stomach acid to enter the oesophagus more easily. Some chocoholics also experience allergic reactions, kidney stones and heartburn.

HIGH COPPER CONSUMPTION
Elevated copper levels, caused by inhibiting sulphur, can adversely affect a person's memory and concentration, so progressive copper storage as a result of long-term high chocolate intake combined with lowered sulphur levels can lead to mental impairment or dementia. Eating large amounts of chocolate for high flavonoid intake to ease some medical problems may therefore have the opposite effect on health. Chocolate's high copper content inhibits some flavonoids from working properly, which could lead to vascular problems like varicose veins, haemorrhoids, bruising, heart disease or stroke. The additional consumption of high copper sources such as chocolate and cocoa products, in addition to coffee, cola drinks, shellfish, liver, soybeans, and many nuts and seeds, aggravates many high copper-related medical conditions but is also responsible for contributing to, or creating new ones.

Copper is an important factor in new blood vessel formation. With the exception of colon cancer, for which copper and calcium offer some protection, most other types of benign or malignant tumours and fibroids are associated with high copper levels. Dark chocolate has the highest catechin content, but also the highest copper level.

MIGRAINE

Some chemicals in chocolate can trigger migraine headaches. Chocolate is not the only food to bring on attacks, but one trial found it was the catalyst in 30% of cases. Caffeine, phenylethylamine and theobromine are the main offenders by altering the cerebral blood flow. The phenylethylamine in chocolate is a particular trigger.Fasting or skipping meals is also a common reason for headache recurrence in migraine sufferers, and if you eat a chocolate bar to fill the gap, you may just make the situation worse.

SLEEP DISORDERS

It has been suggested that a sleep disorder could be aggravated by chocolate. Sufferers unknowingly act out violent nightmares. Rapid eye movement sleep behaviour disorder affects around one in 200 people, mainly men. Sleepers thrash about and shout as they dream. American research suggests that the caffeine in chocolate helps to block a natural process called atonia that paralyses people during dreams. The sleeper is more free to move around than normally. A patient who had received a head injury in an accident was found to have worse symptoms after eating chocolate. Simple solution: don't give him chocolate!

CHROMIUM DEFICIENCY

Chromium is a trace mineral of copper. The high sugar content in high chocolate consumption increases chromium requirements and the resulting high copper, low chromium ratio creates an increased risk of bone loss. It can trigger or worsen inflammatory conditions that may include chronic tonsil infections, rheumatoid-types of arthritis or other problems of the immune system in some individuals.

SULPHUR

Excess copper levels also lower sulphur levels and are a common cause or aggravating factor of osteoarthritis.

LEAD

High lead concentrations in manufactured cocoa and chocolate products have been reported in the USA, one of the highest reported for all food items. This may have an effect on the development of young children.

Trivia and
Fascinating
Facts

WHAT'S IN A NAME?

Quite a lot, apparently. Chocolate bars and confectionery are renamed in some countries. For example Galaxy chocolate is known as Dove in the USA, China, Germany, the Netherlands, France and Greece. Rather confusing if you are using the skin cream, I should imagine. Another thing I've noticed on my travels is that Mars bars are called by different names. The Mars bar was created in 1936 and the international version of the Mars bar has always been different from the US version, as it does not contain almonds. Both versions have a chocolate malt nougat centre with caramel on top and covered in a layer of milk chocolate. The US Mars bar was renamed to Snickers Almond in 2000, which may have been a huge mistake as annual sales reached over $2 billion in 2000, but by 2002 they had almost halved.

The Snickers bar, created in 1930, has a chewy nougat centre with peanuts and caramel on top, all covered with milk chocolate. It was named Snickers after one of the horses of the Mars family who invented the candy, but sold as the Marathon bar in the United Kingdom until 1990.

FRY'S CHOCOLATE CREAM

Fry's Chocolate Cream started life as Cream Sticks in 1853, and then became Cream Bars in 1866. The mould for the chocolate covered cream bars with a secret cream filling was designed by Francis Fry in 1875. Fry's Five Boys Chocolate was advertised in 1885 with photographs by Messrs Poulton & Son (the photographer's son being the model) depicting the following expressions:

Desperation • Pacification
Expectation • Acclamation • Realisation

The boy, who was called Lindsay, had a rag soaked in ammonia put in front of him to achieve 'desperation'. The realisation was that the product was Fry's. The 'Five Boys' picture was used in 1902 when Fry's milk chocolate was launched. It stayed popular until it was withdrawn in 1976.

KIT KAT TRIVIA

- The traditional four-finger version of this bar was developed after a worker at the Rowntree's factory in York put in a suggestion for a snack that a 'man could have in his lunch box for work'. The bar was first launched in 1935 for 2*d*, under the name of Rowntree's Chocolate Crisp.
- The two-finger version was launched in 1936 and renamed in 1937.
- It became a UK favourite with its endorsement by Churchill's wartime government as healthy, cheap food, and maintained its supremacy despite competition.
- In 1945, milk shortages in the UK forced its makers to use plain chocolate and the Kit Kat packaging was blue for a time.
- The current name is believed to have come from the Kit-Cat Club, an 18th-century Whig literary club founded in the reign of James II. The club met at Christopher Catling's pie-house in Shire Lane, Temple Bar. The meeting place had such low ceilings that paintings hung inside needed to be especially short.
- Paintings of this shape became known as 'Kit Kats', as was a type of mutton pie.
- The slogan 'Have A Break — Have A Kit Kat' has been in use since 1957.
- Popular varieties in Germany and Japan include a lemon cheesecake version.

COMMEMORATIVE TINS AND CONTAINERS

These can be worth quite a bit these days, if online auction sites are anything to go by. Special presentations for events such as the Royal Silver Jubilee 1935 Chocolate Tin, Scarborough, and other special boxes, particularly by Rowntree, are highly collectable.

Fry's and Cadbury's presented chocolate assortments in the most elaborate gift boxes and unusual containers until the late 1930s. Some of these were:

- 5 o' clock, where chocolates were packed in a burnished aluminium teapot.
- Antony. Deluxe chocolates presented in a lacquer handkerchief box.

- Nell Gwynne, an oblong grey leatherette box with a metal ornament on a turquoise-blue centrepiece filled with deluxe chocolates.
- Clock Cabinet, a leatherette cabinet fitted with a clock, which could be removed, and four drawers.
- Weekend cases, velvet trinket boxes, stationery cabinets filled with 3 pounds of chocolates plus a whole range of toy novelties for children.

BOURBON BISCUITS
The Bourbon biscuit is a sandwich biscuit consisting of two thin, rectangular, dark chocolate biscuits with a chocolate fondant filling. It was introduced in 1910 (originally under the name Creola) by Peek Freans. It is apparently named after the House of Bourbon, an aristocratic French and Spanish family.

CLIMB EVERY MOUNTAIN
Sir Edmund Hillary ate chocolate when he climbed Mount Everest. I wonder how much.

UNUSUAL SANDWICHES AND SNACKS
A Fry's Cream sandwich is said to be popular with some in the west of Scotland. The bar is chopped into small slices and placed between two slices of bread with margarine or butter. No comment.

Deep fried Mars bars are also said to be popular in Scotland and some other areas of the UK.

CANNABIS MIMIC
A lawyer claimed that his client was innocent of smoking and dealing in marijuana after he was found positive for cannabis in a routine urine screening test. The accused argued that he had eaten a massive amount of chocolate which contained anandamide-related lipids. These lipids act as cannabinoid mimics and, according to the lawyer, were the cause of the positive drugs test. A quick test by scientists and the knowledge that you would have to eat about 11 kg of chocolate to get high, resulted in the conviction of the accused.

18TH-CENTURY CHOCOLATE
This recipe comes from a French recipe book by Menon, published in 1755, snappily entitled:

> *'Les Soupers de la Cour ou l'Art de travailler toutes sortes d'aliments pour servir les meilleures tables suivant les quatre saisons.'*

Which translates as:

> *'Royal Suppers, or the art of using all sorts of foods to serve the best tables according to the time of year / season.'*

> *'Place one tablet of chocolate for each cup of water in a coffee pot and bring it slowly to the boil; when ready to serve, add one egg yolk for every four cups and stir with the baton over a slow fire, without boiling. It is better if made in the evening for the next day. Those who drink it every day save a leaven for the next day's pot. Instead of an egg yolk, a whipped egg white can be used after removing the first froth; blend it with a little chocolate taken from the coffee pot, then put it in the pot and finish off as with a yolk.'*

NO YOLK
If all the Crème Eggs made each year were placed next to each other, they would reach 12,000 miles: from Birmingham to Australia.

CHOCOLATE BLOOD
In 1960, chocolate syrup was used to simulate blood in the famous shower scene in Alfred Hitchcock's movie, *'Psycho'*. The scene took over seven days to shoot.

PRALINE
Chocolate manufacturers today use 40% of the world's almonds. The idea of making praline is attributed to a mistake in 1671. The Duke of Presslis-Praslin was waiting for his dessert. A kitchen boy spilt a bowl of almonds on the floor and the angry chef tried to catch him to give

him a beating. Unfortunately he tripped with a pan of hot, burnt sugar. The creative chef decided to serve the nuts anyway and the duke was delighted with his new dish. I suppose a covering of chocolate was the next logical step.

MY SWEET LORD
A New York gallery angered a US Catholic group with its decision to exhibit a milk chocolate sculpture of Jesus Christ. The 6 ft (1.8 m) sculpture, entitled *'My Sweet Lord'*, of Jesus naked on the cross was created by Canadian artist Cosimo Cavallaro. He upset the Catholic Church by choosing Holy Week to show his sculpture. Mr Cavallaro is known for using food ingredients in his art, on one occasion painting a hotel room in mozzarella cheese. Tasty! He used 90 kg (200 lb) of chocolate to make the sculpture, depicting Jesus without a loincloth. Perhaps he ran out of chocolate . . .

CHOCOLATE TRAVELS
Johann Wolfgang von Goethe travelled through Switzerland in 1797. He insisted that he had chocolate available to drink at all times, so he took his pot with him.

MOST EXPENSIVE CHOCOLATES

Handmade gourmet chocolates are for sale in small amounts to buyers who are rich enough. At up to £40 per pound, these are not for the kids. But these pale into insignificance next to a Knipschildt Madelaine Truffle. Fritz Knipschildt, from Denmark, is Maitre Chocolatier of Knipschildt Chocolatier. He created the 42 g (1.5 oz) gem of a confection.

The ganache is made using French Valrhona Chocolate blended with fresh cream, infused for 24 hours with vanilla pods and pure Italian truffle oil. This has to be repeatedly whipped to make it soft and silky before being chilled. This is then shaped around a French Perigord truffle, known also as French black truffle, costing around £500 per 450 g (1 lb). Next it is dipped in a 70%

cocoa-rich Valrhona dark chocolate, and is finished off with a dusting of cocoa powder.

Each delicate truffle is packaged within a pouch and placed in a silver jewellry box, nestled within red satin, tied in edible sugar pearls, and adorned with a ribbon. Well, you would expect that for the price. Each truffle is then numbered as a limited edition and accompanied by a personal note from its creator. Needless to say, you can't just go into a chocolate shop and buy one, even if you could afford to, or wanted to spend that much money on a chocolate. They are made to order. I've seen a picture of one and they don't look that different from my home-made versions, although I rather think they taste better! Each truffle costs around £125 or $250, making the confection cost approximately £1,300 per pound in quantity.

Single estate or single bean chocolates are pretty expensive, although rather more affordable than the Madeleine. Valrhona Guanaja Dark Bitter will set you back about £3 for 75 g, or Prestat Organic Dark might fill that gap at £9.50 for 200 g. Amedei Tuscany Chuao Extra 70% costs around £4.50 for 100 g.

**20TH-CENTURY TIMELINE OF
SOME POPULAR CHOCOLATE BARS**
Some of the old favourites have been around for a long time. Some are unfortunately, no longer with us.

- 1853 Fry's Chocolate Cream introduced
- 1902 Fry's milk chocolate introduced
- 1905 Cadbury launch Dairy Milk
- 1914 Fry's Turkish Delight introduced
- 1915 Milk Tray introduced
- 1920 Cadbury Flake introduced
- 1923 Cream-filled eggs first introduced
- 1928 Fruit and Nut introduced as a variation of Dairy Milk
  Cadbury 'glass and a half' advertising slogan launched
- 1929 Crunchie launched
- 1930 Snickers bar introduced

- 1933 WholeNut added to the Dairy Milk family
- 1935 Four-finger Chocolate Crisp introduced
  Aero introduced
- 1936 Dairybox introduced
  Quality Street introduced
  Two-finger Chocolate Crisp
  Mars bar introduced
- 1937 Chocolate Crisp renamed Kit Kat
  Rolos introduced
  Smarties introduced
- 1938 Cadbury Roses introduced
- 1957 Munchies introduced
- 1958 Picnic launched
- 1959 Caramac introduced
- 1962 After Eight introduced
- 1967 Golden Cup introduced
- 1968 Matchmakers introduced
- 1970 Breakaway introduced
- 1971 Cadbury Creme Egg launched
- 1976 Yorkie introduced
  Lion Bar introduced
  Caramel launched
- 1980 Drifter is introduced
- 1987 Twirl launched
- 1999 Kit Kat Chunky introduced

Chocolate
Recipes

COOKING WITH CHOCOLATE

This is the part of the book where we stop worrying about whether chocolate is good for you or not and we celebrate some of the fantastic things you can do with it. One of the things my grown-up children remember about Christmas and Easter is that we always used to make mini eggs and tree decorations at home. The fun in making and wrapping tiny foil Santa shapes has stayed with them, apparently. They were much cheaper at the time and you knew what was in them, chocolate-wise.

How about savoury dishes? How does chocolate curry grab you, for instance? Apparently a chef in Birmingham has perfected a sort of creamy chicken korma. Other chefs have used chocolate with venison or other game and in chilli con carne. Chilli was one of the earliest additives to chocolate anyway. In South and Central America, where chocolate originates from, it is used in a whole range of recipes, especially to serve with turkey or chicken.

Even less likely is the idea of lobster with chocolate, although some cheeses (try gorgonzola) seem to go quite well with chocolate.

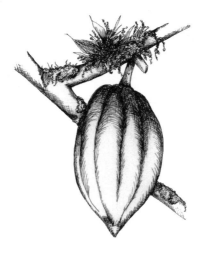

SAVOURY CHOCOLATE RECIPES

LOBSTER WITH CHOCOLATE

Lobster is too expensive to mess about with!

You will need:
    1 medium (1½ pound) fresh lobster
    4 squares dark chocolate, chopped
    50 ml (2 fluid oz) milk
    1 tablespoon butter

Method:
1. Preheat the grill.
2. Split the lobster down the back shell, remove the spinal chord and the sac that is behind the eyes. Insert a long skewer into the tail to keep it from curling.
3. Grill for about 5 minutes on each side, or until the meat is opaque. Remove the skewer from the tail.
4. Meanwhile make the chocolate sauce. Combine the chocolate, milk, and butter in a small pan and heat slowly until the chocolate melts. Pour the sauce over the lobster and serve, or maybe eat the lobster and use the sauce on some ice cream for pudding!

CHICKEN WITH CHOCOLATE AND CHERRY SAUCE

I suppose this isn't so different from poultry or game with cherry sauce, so not quite as unusual.

You will need: Serves 2

    25 g (1 oz) coarse salt
    570 ml (1 pint) water
    2 boneless, skinless chicken breasts
    25 g (1 oz) flour
    12 g (½ oz) butter
    1 tablespoon olive oil
    240 ml (8 fluid oz) chicken stock
    50 g (2 oz) dried cherries
    50 ml (2 fluid oz) balsamic vinegar
    25 g (1 oz) unsweetened chocolate, chopped
    1 tablespoon brandy or orange juice

Method:
1. Mix the salt and water in a bowl. Add the chicken and leave for 30 minutes in the refrigerator.
2. Remove the chicken from the brine, rinse and pat dry.
3. Roll the chicken breasts in flour, patting gently to lightly coat. Leave to rest for 10 to 15 minutes.
4. Heat the butter and oil in a pan over medium heat and cook until the butter begins to brown slightly. Lay the chicken breasts in the pan and cook, undisturbed, until brown, about 5 minutes. Turn the chicken pieces over and cook on the second side, until thoroughly cooked. Remove the chicken and keep warm.
5. Add the chicken stock to the pan, scraping to release any brown bits. Boil until reduced and thickened. Add the cherries and vinegar, stirring for another 5 minutes, or until a spoon scraped across the bottom of the pan leaves a visible path in the sauce. Stir in the chocolate and brandy or orange juice. Serve with the chicken.

CHICKEN OR TURKEY MOLE

This is a popular South American dish, of which there are many variations. I'm a great fan of turkey, a true superfood.

You will need:
    1 dried chilli
    2 tablespoons vegetable oil, goose or duck fat
    1 tablespoon red chillis, ground
    325 ml (12 fluid oz) chicken stock
    2 tortillas, cut in strips, or stale bread
    1 tomato, skinned and chopped
    1 onion, chopped
    ½ tablespoon raisins
    ½ tablespoon flaked almonds
    ½ tablespoon sesame seeds
    ½ tablespoon pumpkin seeds
    1 teaspoon sugar
    1 teaspoon oregano
    25 g (1 oz) dark chocolate
    ¼ teaspoon anise
    ⅛ teaspoon ground cinnamon
    2 cloves
    Pinch nutmeg
    Pinch ground ginger
    ¼ teaspoon cumin seed
    ¼ teaspoon coriander seeds
    4 boneless chicken breast halves, or turkey pieces

Method:
1. Cover the chilli with warm water. Let it stand until softened. Drain and finely chop.
2. Heat the oil or fat in a saucepan over medium heat. Cook and stir the ground red chilli until brown. Add a drop of water to prevent scorching if necessary. Allow to cool and then stir in two-thirds of the chicken stock.
3. Stir in remaining ingredients except the remaining stock and chicken or turkey. Heat to boiling, reduce the heat and cover. Simmer for 30 minutes, stirring occasionally. Allow to cool.
4. Place a small amount of the sauce into a blender. Cover and blend on high speed until smooth. Repeat with

the remaining sauce.

5. Heat 100 ml (4 fluid oz) of the sauce and the remaining chicken stock in a 12-inch skillet. Place the chicken in a single layer in the skillet. Cover and simmer until done, about 20 minutes. Remove the chicken to a serving dish and keep warm.

6. In a skillet combine some of the cooking liquid with the remaining sauce and heat to boiling, stirring constantly. Pour over the chicken and serve.

CHILLI CON CARNE WITH CHOCOLATE

You will need: Serves 4

450 g (1 lb) lean mince
1 tablespoon tomato purée
2 tablespoons olive oil
1 onion, chopped
1 clove garlic, crushed
1 tin red kidney beans
½ tin tomatoes
Salt and black pepper
1 red chilli, deseeded and chopped
½ teaspoon ground coriander
¼ to ½ teaspoon chilli powder, to taste
1 teaspoon ground cumin
½ teaspoon ground cinnamon
275 ml (10 fluid oz) vegetable stock
25 g (1 oz) unsweetened chocolate

Method:

1. In a large bowl, season the mince with pepper and salt to taste. Add the cinnamon, cumin, coriander and chilli powder. Mix well.

2. Preheat a saucepan over medium high heat. Add the olive oil and then the coated meat, spreading it evenly so it covers the bottom. Leave to brown well.

3. Add the oil and the onions, chilli and garlic. Sauté for 5 minutes over medium heat. Add the tomato paste, tinned tomatoes and the stock. Stir well. Simmer for 30 to 40 minutes.

4. Strain the juice from the kidney beans and add to the

pot with more salt and pepper if necessary. Add chunks of chocolate. Stir until it melts and serve immediately. Serve with grated cheese, rice, green salad and sour cream.

CHOCOLATE DRINK RECIPES

COSI FAN TUTTE CHOCOLATE

This can be made, with care, in a microwave, but be careful not to overheat the chocolate.

Per cup you will need:
50—80 g (2—3 oz) dark chocolate
1 teaspoon caster sugar
Pinch of salt
1 cup whole milk
½ teaspoon vanilla extract
whipped cream for serving

Method:
1. Break the chocolate into small pieces and put into a bowl with the sugar and salt to melt.
2. In a medium saucepan, heat the milk over medium-low heat to just under the boil. Add the chocolate mixture and continue cooking, stirring constantly, until the mixture thickens slightly. Remove from the heat and whisk in the vanilla.
3. Pour into a mug, top with softly whipped cream and serve immediately.

CHOCOLATE MALTED MILK

Per cup you will need:
1 cup cocoa or hot chocolate
1 tablespoon cream
1 tablespoon malted milk powder

Method:
1. Make the hot chocolate or cocoa and mix in the malted milk powder.
2. Serve with the cream on top.

HOT MOCHA CHOCOLATE

This creamy hot drink is simple to make

You will need: Serves 3—4
    570 ml (1 pint) milk
    25 g (1 oz) semi-sweet chocolate
    175 ml (6 fluid oz)) strong hot coffee
    Sugar to taste
    Whipped cream

Method:
1. Bring the milk to simmering point. Add the chocolate, stirring constantly until it melts.
2. Stir in the coffee and sugar to taste. Pour into cups and top with whipped cream.

HOT COFFEE WITH AMARETTO AND CHOCOLATE

Per cup you will need:
    1 tablespoon dark Creme de Cacao, or similar
    225 ml (8 oz) hot black coffee
    2 tablespoons Amaretto
    Whipped cream and grated chocolate for garnish

Method:
1. Mix the liqueurs in a cup and pour over the coffee.
2. Decorate with whipped cream and chocolate on the top.

PEPPERMINT HOT CHOCOLATE

Per cup you will need:
    42 g (1½ oz) peppermint schnapps
    1 tablespoon whipped cream
    1 cup hot chocolate, made with water

Method:
1. Mix the peppermint schnapps with the hot chocolate in a cup.
2. Decorate the cup with whipped cream.

HOT CHOCOLATE WITH ORANGE

You will need: **Serves 2**

    450 ml (16 fluid oz) milk
    110 g (4 oz) chocolate, chopped
    2–3 orange peel strips, without the pith
    ½ teaspoon instant coffee powder
    Pinch of ground cinnamon

Method:
1. Stir all of the ingredients together over a low heat until the chocolate melts. Increase the heat and bring just to the boil, stirring often.
2. Remove from heat and whisk until frothy. Return to the heat and whisk again.
3. Remove the orange peel and pour the chocolate into mugs.

PARISIAN HOT CHOCOLATE

This French version is very strong and best served in small amounts.

You will need: **Serves 3—4**

    225 ml (8 fluid oz) whole milk
    80 ml (3 fluid oz) double cream
    25 g (1 oz) granulated sugar
    150 g (5 oz) dark, good quality chocolate, chopped or grated
    Whipped cream and cinnamon, to garnish

Method:
1. Heat together the milk, double cream and sugar until simmering.
2. Remove the pan from the heat and add the chocolate, stirring to melt it. Return the pan to a low heat, stirring constantly until all the chocolate has melted. The mixture should be smooth, evenly coloured and hot.
3. Serve warm in small cups with whipped cream and cinnamon.

HOT CHOCOLATE FLOAT

This is an unusual mix of hot and cold: not to everyone's choice, especially if you have sensitive teeth.

Per cup you will need:
1 cup of hot chocolate
1 scoop ice cream, any flavour

Method:
1. Make the hot chocolate and top with a scoop of ice cream.

BRANDIED CHOCOLATE VELVET

You will need: Serves 2
50 g (2 oz) milk chocolate, broken up
50 ml (2 fluid oz) double cream
1 tablespoon cocoa powder
2 tablespoons brandy, or whisky
225 ml (8 fluid oz) milk
Whipped cream and chocolate curls for topping

Method:
1. Whip the cream until fairly thick.
2. Put the milk into a saucepan and add the cocoa powder. Add the broken chocolate and heat gently until the chocolate melts, stirring.
3. Bring the milk to the boil. Remove from the heat and whisk in the cream and brandy. Stir to blend.
4. Serve in heatproof glasses or cups, topped with whipped cream and chocolate curls.

MEXICAN HOT CHOCOLATE (CHAMPURRADO)

I have included this recipe for interest, although I have
no personal experience of making chocolate this way.
It seems, apart from the sugar, the nearest thing to what
the Aztecs may have drunk.

You will need: Serves 6
   6 cups of water
   2 cinnamon sticks
   80 g (3 oz) masa harina (Mexican maize flour)
   175 g (6 oz) brown sugar
   25 g (1 oz) unsweetened chocolate
   1 teaspoon vanilla extract

Method:
1. Combine 4 cups of the water and cinnamon in a
saucepan. Bring to the boil.
2. Place the remaining water and flour in a blender until
smooth. Pour the mixture through a fine mesh sieve into
the cinnamon water.
3. Bring to the boil and then reduce the heat to low,
stirring constantly with a whisk, for 6 to 7 minutes or
until the mixture is thickened.
4. Stir in the sugar, chocolate and vanilla extract. Cook,
stirring frequently, until the chocolate is melted and the
flavours have blended.

CHILLED CHOCOLATE

You will need: **Serves 4—6**

   225 g (8 oz) unsweetened chocolate
   1 litre (35 fluid oz) boiled water
   25—50 g (1—2 oz) sugar, according to taste
   2 tablespoons cherry liqueur (optional)
   150 ml (5 fluid oz) whipped cream
   100 ml (4 fluid oz) milk
   1 tablespoon grated chocolate

Method:

1. Melt the chocolate in a bowl over some warm water. Add 3 tablespoons of hot water, stirring with a wire whisk to get an even consistency.
2. Add the remaining hot water and the sugar. Stir until thoroughly blended.
3. Pour into a pitcher with the milk. Refrigerate for two hours or until cold.
4. Stir in the liqueur and pour into tall glasses, topping each with whipped cream and grated chocolate.

CHOCOLATE AND BANANA BREAKFAST DRINK

My dietary needs don't allow such luxuries, but this may be a special treat. You can add peanut butter as well, if you like it, but my family are not fans.

Per cup you will need:

   1 cup readymade chocolate drink, cold
   ½ banana, chopped
   4 ice cubes
   1 tablespoon peanut butter (optional)

Method:

1. Place the ingredients in a blender until smooth. Serve immediately

CHOCOLATE FRAPPÉ

Per cup you will need:
  ½ cup strong cocoa, made with water
  ½ cup chilled sparkling water
  Ice cubes

Method:
1. Make the cocoa and let it cool completely.
2. Add the sparkling water just before drinking and serve with ice cubes.

CHOCOLATE AND BANANA MILKSHAKE

You will need: Serves 3—4
  450 ml (16 fluid oz) vanilla ice cream, slightly softened
  125 ml (4 fluid oz) milk
  1 medium banana, sliced
  4—6 tablespoons drinking chocolate mix

Method:
1. Place all the ingredients in a blender and whisk until smooth.
2. Pour into glasses and serve.

FROZEN MUDSLIDES

Definitely one for the adults. This will make two alcoholic drinks.

You will need: Serves 2
  1 shot vodka
  1 shot coffee liqueur
  1 shot Irish cream liqueur
  2 to 3 scoops vanilla ice cream, slightly softened

Method:
1. Place all of the ingredients into a blender and whisk until smooth.
2. Serve immediately.

CHOCOLATE DESSERT RECIPES

Several of these recipes come from old sources from France, as well as the UK. I offer them as alternatives to the usual chocolate desserts which are so familiar today. One of the interesting things is the method of making the sauces. This relies on good quality dark, high cocoa content: not everyday cooking chocolate or milk chocolate, which won't give nearly such delicious results. Many are not for the faint hearted, as they contain copious amounts of raw or partially cooked eggs and quantities of cream. You can, of course, leave out some of the eggs or use low fat cream varieties.

Recipes have been adapted from both metric and imperial quantities, so the equivalents may vary from one recipe to another. As long as you don't mix metric and imperial, there should be no problem.

SOUFFLÉ WITH CHOCOLATE SAUCE

This old French recipe can be simplified by using a microwave for the first two stages. You could make individual portions in rammekin dishes or crème brûlée dishes. A quicker way is to use the soufflé omelette recipe, on the next page.

You will need: Serves 4—6
     25 g (1 oz) flour
     150 ml (5 fluid oz) milk
     25 g (1 oz) sugar
     25 g (1 oz) butter
     3 egg yolks
     4 egg whites
     225 g (8 oz) chocolate (70% cocoa solids)
     425 ml (15 fluid oz) water
     1 tablespoon sugar
     3 tablespoons cream
     knob of butter

Method:
1. Preheat the oven to 180°C (350°F, gas mark 4). Butter a soufflé dish, or dishes, and sprinkle with sugar.
2. Mix the flour with a little of the milk. Heat the rest of

the milk with the sugar in a large pan.

3. Add the flour mix and stir until the milk boils. Keep simmering for 2 minutes. Remove from the heat and stir in the butter and egg yolks. Beat well.

4. Beat the egg whites until stiff and fold into the batter.

5. Pour the batter into the prepared dish(es) and bake until risen (about 20 minutes).

6. Meanwhile, make the sauce by dissolving the chocolate in the water over a low heat. Add the sugar and simmer gently for 20 minutes. Add the cream and knob of butter. Pour over the soufflé and serve.

SOUFFLÉ OMELETTE WITH BANANA AND CHOCOLATE FILLING

Chocolate filled pancakes and sweet omelettes are a real treat. You can fill them with anything of course, but I always think banana and chocolate is good. Use the filling for either the pancakes or omelettes.

For 2 sweet omelettes you will need:
>   2 eggs, separated
>   1 tablespoon caster sugar
>   1 tablespoon butter

Method:

1. Beat the egg yolks with the sugar until creamy. Beat the egg whites until stiff.

2. Fold the egg whites into the yolks.

3. Heat the butter in a pan until bubbling. Pour in the egg mixture and spread evenly over the pan. Cook for about 3 to 4 minutes, then put the pan under a medium hot grill for about 5 minutes. Remove from heat.

4. Spread with chosen filling, fold the omelette in half and serve immediately.

BANANA AND CHOCOLATE FILLING

You will need: Serves 2
  1—2 bananas
  50 g (2 oz) dark chocolate
  1 tablespoon honey

Method:
1. Warm the honey and chocolate together to melt. Add the sliced banana and cook for 2 to 3 minutes over a gentle heat.
2. Spread over omelette or pancake, fold over and serve warm.

PANCAKE MIX (CREPES)

You will need for 8 pancakes:
  50 g (2 oz) butter
  100 g (4 oz) flour
  2 eggs
  200 ml (8 fluid oz) milk

Method:
1. Melt the butter and leave to cool.
2. Sift flour into a bowl. Add the eggs and gradually the milk and butter until you have a smooth batter.
3. Grease a pan and when hot, pour enough batter in to just cover the bottom. Tilt the pan to spread evenly.
4. Cook until the underside is brown, toss or turn over quickly and fry the other side.
5. Pile up on a plate, with greaseproof paper between them, until all the batter has been cooked. Fill with favourite chocolate mix and enjoy!

CHOCOLATE VELVET SAUCE

Extremely luxurious and very sweet.
You will need:
  25 g (1 oz) chocolate
  100 g (4 oz) caster sugar
  3 tablespoons boiling water

1 tablespoon butter
100 g (4 oz) marshmallows, chopped

Method:
1. Melt the chocolate with the water. Add the butter and stir to a smooth paste.
2. Stir in the sugar and cook to thicken slightly. Add the marshmallows and stir to blend. Serve hot.

SAUCE FOR ICE CREAM

You will need:
80 g (3 oz) dark, unsweetened chocolate
1 cup icing sugar
1 cup evaporated milk
½ cup water

Method:
1. Melt the chocolate in a heatproof bowl standing in a pan of water, or in the top of a double pan. Stir in the sugar and milk.
2. Keep stirring until fully blended and all the sugar has dissolved.
3. Serve warm, over ice cream or chosen dessert.

PEARS WITH CHOCOLATE SAUCE

This is an easy dessert and quite nice, if you like pears. It reminds me of old-style restaurants and visiting elderly relatives for Sunday lunch, only we didn't get the hot chocolate sauce!

You will need: Serves 4
4 pears
150 ml (5 fluid oz) water
50 g (2 oz) sugar
100 g (4 oz) dark chocolate
25 g (1 oz) butter

Method:
1. Pare the pears and cut into quarters. Remove any cores.
2. Heat the water and dissolve the sugar in a pan. Add the pears and poach for about 10 minutes, until tender. Drain the pears and place in an ovenproof dish, keeping 2 tablespoons of the juice for the sauce.
3. Preheat the oven to 180°C (350°F, gas mark 4).
4. Break the chocolate and melt it in a bowl over a pan of hot water. Stir in the butter and the pear syrup.
5. Pour the sauce over the pears, cover with foil and bake for about 10 minutes. Serve hot, with vanilla ice cream.

VERY RICH CHOCOLATE SAUCE

This is fine if you aren't on a limited cholesterol or sugar diet! Also, the partially cooked eggs might pose a problem.

You will need:
>80 g (3 oz) dark chocolate
>2 eggs, separated
>300 ml (10 fluid oz) milk
>80 g (3 oz) castor sugar

Method:
1. Break the chocolate into a bowl over a pan of water or in the top of a double pan. Add 50 g (2 oz) of the sugar and milk and heat, stirring frequently.
2. Add the egg yolks, one at a time and stir well to thicken. Don't allow this to boil.
3. Whisk the egg whites until stiff and add the rest of the sugar.
4. Pour the chocolate sauce over the egg whites and stir to mix.
Serve at once.

COLD CHOCOLATE AND ORANGE SOUFFLÉ

This recipe uses gelatine to set the soufflé, but you can substitute a vegetarian variety. Also, you can use Elmlea whipping cream to lighten the fat load. If you have some orange liqueur, you can add a tablesponful to the cream for decorating and serving.

You can use a microwave for the first part of this recipe, but don't allow the mixture to boil. Microwaves vary, so follow the directions in your instruction book.

You will need:
> 175 g (6 oz) dark chocolate
> 3 egg yolks
> 4 egg whites
> 425 ml (15 fluid oz) semi-skimmed milk
> 1 tablespoon gelatine or substitute
> Juice and grated rind of an orange
> 50 g (2 oz) sugar
> 300 ml (10 fluid oz) whipping cream

Method:
1. Grease and line a large soufflé dish, with a generous additional collar of paper.
2. Put the milk into a pan and break all but a square of the chocolate into it. Heat gently to melt the chocolate and then increase the heat to near boiling.
3. Whisk the egg yolks with the sugar. Gradually pour over the milk mixture and stir well. Return the mix to the pan and continue to heat, but not boil, until the mix thickens slightly. This may take time, so be patient.
4. Mix the gelatine or substitute with a little (3 tablespoons) water in a bowl and leave to soak. Place the bowl over a pan of water until the gelatine has dissolved.
5. Stir the dissolved gelatine with the orange juice and rind and add to the soufflé. Allow to cool.
6. Whisk the eggs whites until stiff and then the cream. Fold the egg whites and all but a little of the cream into the soufflé. Pour into the prepared dish and leave to set.
7. To serve, carefully remove the collar of paper. Decorate with the remaining cream and grated chocolate.

GEM'S CHOCOLATE ROULADE

A true family favourite, and my daughter's signature dish.

You will need:
- 60 g (4 tablespoons) cocoa powder
- 150 ml (5 fluid oz) milk
- 4 eggs, separated
- 100 g (4 oz) caster sugar
- 225 ml (8 fluid oz) double cream

Method:
1. Grease and line a Swiss roll tin. Mix the cocoa powder and milk in a small saucepan and heat until the cocoa has dissolved. Remove pan and let milk cool.
2. Whisk the egg yolks and sugar together until pale and fluffy. Whisk the cooled milk into the egg mixture.
3. Whisk the egg whites until stiff and fold into the mixture. Spread evenly into the Swiss roll tin and bake at 180°C (350°F, gas mark 4) for about 20 minutes, until firm to the touch.
4. Turn out onto a sheet of greaseproof and cover with a warm, damp tea towel. Leave to cool for 20 minutes.
5. Whip the cream until stiff. Spread over the sponge, reserving some for decoration, and roll up carefully. Don't worry if it cracks. Serve with cream and strawberries on top.

CHOCOLATE CHESTNUT MOUSSE

This used to be a hot favourite in our house, before the need to cut back on the eggs. Using chestnut purée makes the whole thing manageable and very good at Christmas time, especially if you have half a tin left over from chestnut stuffing.

You will need: **Serves 6—8**
- 400 g (14 oz) tin chestnut purée
- 150 g (5 oz) plain chocolate
- 4 eggs, separated
- 150 ml (5 fluid oz) whipping cream

Method:

1. Place the chestnut purée in a bowl over a pan of hot water with the broken chocolate pieces. When melted, remove from the heat.
2. Stir in the egg yolks, one at a time and beat well.
3. Whip the cream and whisk the egg whites. Fold into the chestnut mix.
4. Pour into individual glasses or dishes and refrigerate until needed.

MOUSSE AU CHOCOLAT

The benefit of this version is that there are no eggs involved. You could use flavoured chocolate, as long as it is of good quality. Alternatively, you could add some liqueur.

You will need: **Serves 4**

    100 g (4 oz) grated bitter chocolate
    300 ml (10 fluid oz) whipping cream
    100 g (4 oz) castor sugar
    300 ml (10 fluid oz) water
    1 teaspoon vanilla essence (optional)

Method:

1. Put the water, vanilla, sugar and chocolate into a saucepan and heat gently until the sugar has dissolved and the chocolate has melted. Remove from the heat and allow to cool.
2. Whip the cream and add most of it to the chocolate mix. Fold together and pour into serving dishes. Chill thoroughly before serving, garnished with a swirl of cream and chocolate flakes.

CHOCOLATE CREAM MACAROON DESSERTS

These are quick to make and will happily sit in the fridge until required.

You will need: Serves 4

    8 macaroon biscuits
    2 tablespoons rum
    50 g (2 oz) butter
    50 g (2 oz) caster sugar
    75 ml (3 fluid oz) milk
    225 g (8 oz) chocolate

Method:
1. Place 4 of the macaroons in the bottom of serving dishes and drizzle over the rum.
2. Cream the butter and sugar together. Boil the milk and allow to cool for 10 minutes.
3. Put the chocolate, broken into pieces, in a bowl over a pan of hot water to melt. Add to the milk with the butter and sugar. Beat until smooth.
4. Pour half of the sauce into the dishes, add another macaroon and top up with the remaining sauce.
5. Refrigerate for 12 hours before serving.

MOCHA CREAM

This very adult dessert certainly got the thumbs up when friends came for lunch. I used 99% cocoa solid chocolate, which was too bitter to eat from the bar, even for me. The result was a very chocolaty, not overly sweet coffee chocolate sensation! I used crème fraiche instead of whipping cream, because it is very hard to find in France, unless you use Chantilly cream. The result was fine.

You will need: Serves 4

    150 g (5 oz) chocolate
    3 tablespoons strong black coffee,
        sweetened or not, to taste
    3 eggs, separated
    142 ml (5 fluid oz) whipping cream

Method:

1. Break the chocolate into a basin with the coffee over a pan of warm water until the chocolate melts. Remove from the heat.

2. Beat in the egg yolks, one at a time.

3. Whisk the egg whites and the cream. Fold these into the chocolate mix.

4. Pour into dishes and chill for one hour.

PROFITEROLES

Another family favourite, these are not hard to make, especially if you dispense with the piping bag that some recipes suggest. Choux pastry is easy to make, once you get the hang of it. The mini buns can be plain, or slightly spicy, with added flavours. You can soup up the chocolate sauce, too, if you like, with some favourite liqueur.

You will need: **Serves 6**

    For the choux pastry:

    80 g (3 oz) plain flour

    50 g (2 oz) butter

    2 eggs, beaten

    150 ml (5 fluid oz) water

    1 teaspoon ground cinnamon (optional)

    For the cream filling:

    300 ml (10 fluid oz) whipping cream

    1 tablespoon icing sugar (optional)

    2 teaspoons strong coffee (optional)

    For the chocolate sauce:

    120 g (4 oz) dark chocolate

    2 tablespoons golden syrup

    2 tablespoons liqueur (optional)

Method:

1. Preheat the oven to 200°C (400°F, gas mark 6). Grease a baking sheet or two.

2. Sift the flour (and cinnamon, if using). Put the water into a saucepan with the butter and heat gently until the butter melts. Increase the heat when all the butter has melted and bring to the boil.

3. Remove from the heat and add the flour, quickly

beating in with a wooden spoon. Mix until smooth.

4. Return to a low heat and continue to beat until the mix forms a dough and leaves the sides of the pan. Remove from the heat and cool slightly.

5. Add the beaten egg, a little at a time, until you have a smooth, glossy dough.

6. Take walnut-sized balls of dough with two spoons and place on the baking sheet(s), allowing room to rise.

7. Bake for 20 minutes, then reduce the heat to 180°C (350°F, gas mark 4) and cook until the buns have risen and sound hollow when tapped (about 15 minutes).

8. Remove to a wire tray to cool and make a slit in each bun to allow steam to escape.

9. Whip the cream and add the icing sugar and coffee essence, if using. Fill each bun, when cool, with cream, using a teaspoon. Arrange on a serving dish or in individual bowls.

10. Melt the chocolate with the syrup and optional alcohol. Stir well and pour over the profiteroles to serve. Delicious!

CHOCOLATE TRUFFLE CREAM

As an experiment, I served this with the Mocha Cream, as an alternative. It was much easier and very straightforward. My friends devoured it as quickly as the first one! Again, I used low fat (15%) crème fraiche and 70% cocoa chocolate. Using cocoa to dust the top keeps the sugar down, but most people would refer the slight sweetness of chocolate powder on the top.

You will need: **Serves 4**
    80 g (3 oz) dark chocolate (at least 70% cocoa solids)
    225 ml (8 fluid oz) whipping cream or crème fraiche
    2 tablespoons cocoa or chocolate powder

Method:
1. Break the chocolate into small pieces and melt in a bowl over hot water.
2. Lightly whip the cream or crème fraiche with a fork and warm slightly. Add to the melted chocolate and stir together.
3. Put in a bowl, mould or individual dishes and chill for at least an hour.
4. If using a mould, remove the tin by placing it on a hot tea towel or standing in a dish of very hot water for 2 minutes before attempting to turn out.
5. Dust with cocoa or chocolate powder to serve.

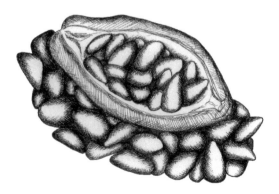

CHOCOLATE FONDUE

You will need: **Serves 4**
    4 tablespoons single cream
    2–3 tablespoons cognac or Grand Marnier
    2 tablespoons grated orange peel
    225 g (8 oz) broken pieces of dark chocolate

You will need for dipping:
    A selection of fresh fruit, e.g. fresh strawberries, thinly
    sliced apples or pears, sliced bananas, fresh tangerine
    segments, sliced star fruit, pineapple chunks. My daughter
    tells me that frozen raspberries, almost thawed, work very
    well. Cubes of cake are also good and so are marshmallows,
    but you have to be quick, otherwise they melt.

Method:
1. Bring the cream and grated orange peel to a simmer in
a heavy medium saucepan and then reduce heat to low.
2. Add broken chocolate and 1 tablespoon of the alcohol.
Whisk until the mixture is smooth. Remove the sauce
from the heat.
3. Blend in the remaining alcohol. Transfer the sauce to a
fondue pot, over a candle or canned heat burner. Serve
with cake pieces and fruit for dipping.

CHOCOLATE ICE CREAM (WITH EGGS)

Again, using a microwave will cut down the time for the
first two parts of this recipe. Use the directions in the
manual for power levels. The use of raw egg means that
care should be taken with consumption and that you
should use the ice cream within a week or two.

You will need: **Serves 4–6**
    100 g (4 oz) bitter chocolate
    300 ml (10 fluid oz) semi-skimmed milk
    3 egg yolks
    50 g (2 oz) sugar
    300 ml (10 fluid oz) whipping cream or Elmlea

Method:

1. Put the milk and broken chocolate pieces into a saucepan over a low heat until the chocolate melts. Increase the heat to almost boiling point.

2. Whisk the egg yolks and sugar together and pour over the chocolate milk. Return the mix to the pan and continue to heat, but not boil, until the mix thickens slightly. This may take time, so be patient.

3. Cool and pour into a shallow freezer dish or ice cream container. When thoroughly cool, cover and freeze for about 2 hours. It will be partially frozen by then.

4. Remove from the container and beat with a fork or whisk to break up any ice crystals. Whip the cream and fold into the frozen mixture.

5. Freeze for another 2 hours at least. Remove from the freezer in plenty of time before serving.

LOW FAT
CHOCOLATE ICE CREAM (WITHOUT EGGS)

This is an adapted, older recipe, producing a denser texture.

You will need:
>   570 ml (1 pint) single cream
>   225 ml (8 fluid oz) skimmed milk
>   175 g (6 oz) caster sugar
>   175 g (6 oz) chocolate

Method:

1. Melt the chocolate in a bowl over warm water with the sugar, until dissolved.

2. Mix in the milk and cream. Stir well and pour into a plastic tub. Cover and freeze for 30 minutes.

3. Remove from freezer, stir well again and replace lid. Return to freezer and freeze thoroughly.

CAKE, BISCUIT & SWEET RECIPES

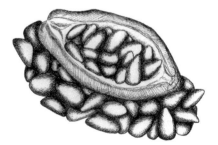

MAHOGANY LAYER CAKE

You will need:
- ½ cup butter
- 2 eggs
- 1 cup milk
- 1¼ cups sugar
- 2½ cups flour
- 1 teaspoon cinnamon
- ¼ teaspoon salt
- 1 teaspoon nutmeg
- 4 teaspoons baking powder
- 1 tablespoon cocoa
- 1 tablespoon cold water

Method:
1. Preheat the oven to 180°C (350°F, gas mark 4). Prepare three cake tins of the same size.
2. Cream together the butter and sugar. Beat the eggs and add to the butter.
3. Sift the flour with the salt, spices and baking powder. Add to the bowl with a little of the milk.
4. Divide the mixture into three. Mix the cocoa and water. Put two parts into the baking tins and add the cocoa to the third part. Then add to the two tins.
5. Bake in the oven for about 20 minutes, until risen. Cool on a wire tray. Decorate and fill with chocolate butter icing or desired topping.

FUDGE FROSTING FOR CAKES

You will need:
- 100 g (4 oz) caster sugar
- 1 teaspoon butter
- 50 g (2 oz) chocolate
- 150 ml (5 fluid oz) milk
- pinch cinnamon

Method:
1. Melt the butter in a saucepan over a low heat and add the sugar and milk. Stir well. Add the chocolate and cinnamon. Increase the temperature and bring to the

boil. Simmer without stirring for 10 minutes.

2. Remove from the heat and beat to a good consistency. Use as required.

CHOCOLATE NOUGAT CAKE

You will need:

50 g (2 oz) butter

1 egg

1 cup milk

3 teaspoons baking powder

225 g (8 oz) flour

225 g (8 oz) caster sugar

50 g (2 oz) caster sugar

50 g (2 oz) melted chocolate

50 g (2 oz) flaked almonds

Method:

1. Prepare a greased and lined tin (20–22 cm, 8–9 inches) and preheat the oven to 180°C (350°F, gas mark 4).

2. Cream the butter with the larger quantity of sugar. Mix well and then add ⅔ of the milk, the sifted flour and baking powder.

3. Stir the melted chocolate with the rest of the sugar in a small pan. Place on the heat and add the rest of the milk. Stir until smooth. Cool slightly.

4. Add to the main cake mix with the almonds and put into the prepared tin. Bake for 15 to 20 minutes.

MARBLE CAKE

This reminds me of one of the better school dinner puddings we used to get, served with chocolate custard. There's an idea . . .

You will need:

80 g (3 oz) butter or margarine, melted

4 eggs

100 g (4 oz) caster sugar

80 g (3 oz) plain flour, sifted

1 tablespoon cocoa, sifted

Vanilla essence, to taste

Method:
1. Grease and line a 17 cm (7 inch) cake tin and preheat the oven to 180°C (350°F, gas mark 4).
2. Put the eggs into a large bowl with the sugar. Place over a pan of hot water and beat them until they are thick and fluffy. Remove from the heat and whisk for a further 2 minutes.
3. Fold in the melted butter and all but one tablespoon of flour. Divide the mix into two.
4. Add the cocoa to one half and the rest of the flour with some vanilla essence to the other.
5. Put heaped spoonfuls of the mixtures into the prepared tin alternately. Bake for about 50 minutes, until the top is golden and springy.
6. Cool on a rack in the tin for a few minutes before turning out to cool completely. Decorate as you wish, or turn into a pudding with a chocolatey sauce.

RICH, DARK CHOCOLATE CAKE

You will need:
80 g (3 oz) self raising-flour
1 tablespoon cocoa powder
100 g (4 oz) chocolate
3 tablespoons water
100 g (4 oz) butter or margarine
100 g (4 oz) caster sugar
4 eggs, separated
For the filling:
Apricot jam

Method:
1. Preheat the oven to 180°C (350°F, gas mark 4) and prepare a 20 cm (8 inch) cake tin.
2. Sift the flour and cocoa together. Break the chocolate and melt in a bowl with the water over a gentle heat. Leave aside to cool slightly.
3. Cream the butter or margarine with the sugar and beat in the egg yolks, one at a time. Fold in the flour and cocoa with the cooled, melted chocolate.
4. Whisk the egg whites and fold into the cake mixture. Turn into the prepared tin and bake for about 50 minutes,

or until the cake is springy when touched. Cool in the tin for a few minutes and then turn out onto a wire tray to cool completely. Divide into three layers and put apricot jam between each layer and over the top of the cake.

You will need for the icing:
>150 g (5 oz) icing sugar
>1 tablespoon cocoa
>50 g (2 oz) plain chocolate
>50 g (2 oz) butter or margarine
>2 tablespoons milk

Method:
1. Sift together the icing sugar and the cocoa.
2. Break the chocolate into a bowl and melt with the butter and milk over some hot water. Stir in the sugar and cocoa.
3. Spread over the top of the cake and leave to set.

LIGHT CHOCOLATE CAKE

This all-in-one cake is simple to bake and delicious when served with vanilla ice cream and chocolate sauce.

You will need:
>225 g (8 oz) plain flour
>225 g (8 oz) sugar
>150 g (5 oz) cocoa
>1½ teaspoons bicarbonate of soda
>1½ teaspoons baking powder
>1 teaspoon salt
>2 eggs, beaten
>225 ml (8 fluid oz) milk
>125 ml (4 fluid oz) canola oil
>2 teaspoons vanilla extract
>225 ml (8 fluid oz) boiling water

Method:
1. Prepare a rectangular baking tray and preheat the oven to 180°C (350°F, gas mark 4).
2. Place all the ingredients except the boiling water in a mixing bowl. Combine until smooth and then add the water.

3. Bake for about 25–30 minutes. Cool on a wire tray and serve with ice cream and chocolate sauce.

EGYPTIAN CHOCOLATE CAKE

You will need:
    100 g (4 oz) squares semi-sweet chocolate
    175 g (6 oz) butter
    100 ml (4 fluid oz) strong black coffee
    275 g (10 oz) sugar
    3 eggs
    1 teaspoon vanilla essence
    225 g (8 oz) plain flour
    1 teaspoon ground cinnamon
    Pinch of ground cloves
    1 teaspoon baking powder
    ½ teaspoon bicarbonate of soda
    100 ml (4 fluid oz) skimmed milk

Method:
1. Preheat the oven to 180°C (350°F, gas mark 4) and grease two 23 cm (9 inch) tins.
2. Melt the chocolate, coffee and butter in a large bowl over warm water or heat in the microwave on medium for 2 to 3 minutes. Stir until smooth.
3. Stir in the sugar. Beat in the eggs, one at a time, and add the vanilla.
4. Sift the dry ingredients together and fold into the other bowl, along with the milk.
5. Pour into the prepared tins and bake for 30 minutes or until the cake springs back when lightly pressed in the centre. Cool for 15 minutes in the tins.
6. Cool on a rack completely before icing.

For the cinnamon whipped cream you will need:
    225 ml (8 fluid oz) whipping cream
    50 ml (2 oz) icing sugar
    ½ teaspoon ground cinnamon

Method:
1. Combine the cream, sugar and cinnamon in a large mixing bowl. Beat on high speed using an electric mixer

until soft peaks form and the mixture is thick enough to spread.

2. Fill and ice the cake with the cinnamon cream. Sprinkle coarsely grated chocolate on top.

CHOCOLATE, WALNUT AND DATE BROWNIES

This is a superior, adult version of a traditional recipe. I used 85% cocoa solids chocolate and the cakes were delicious without being oversweet: an instant hit with the grown-up family. You can make one large cake and cut into squares when cool, or use paper cases for individual brownies.

You will need: **Makes approx 16**

225 g (8 oz) plain chocolate or chocolate chips

80 g (3 oz) chopped dates with 6 tablespoons water

1 tablespoon baking powder

½ teaspoon bicarbonate of soda

60 g (2 oz) soft brown sugar

1 medium egg, beaten

175 g (6 oz) self-raising flour

3 tablespoons skimmed milk

40 g (1½ oz) pecan nuts or walnuts

Method:

1. Preheat the oven to 180°C (350°F, gas mark 4). Grease a baking tin.

2. Melt the chocolate over a pan of simmering water or in a microwave. Place the dates in a pan with the water, and simmer gently until they soften.

3. Sift the flour, baking powder and bicarbonate of soda into a bowl. Add the egg, milk, sugar and nuts.

4. Mix all the ingredients, including the chocolate and the date purée in a large bowl. This will be quite a sloppy batter.

5. Put small spoonfuls into cases or onto the prepared tin. Bake in the oven for 15–20 minutes, until just firm to the touch, before cooling on a wire tray.

CHOCOLATE SPONGE CAKE (EGGLESS)

Bicarbonate of soda can be used to replace eggs in a recipe, so if you have a reason not to eat eggs this might well be the answer. The basic recipe can be flavoured with other things, such as fresh lemon juice and zest or coffee and nuts. Since I can't eat a lot of cakes, I'm afraid chocolate always gets my vote.

You will need:
>   175 g (6 oz) self-raising flour
>   2 heaped teaspoons baking powder
>   25 g (1 oz) cocoa
>   80 g (3 oz) sugar
>   125 ml (4 fluid oz) melted margarine
>   325 ml (11 fluid oz) cold water

Method:
1. Preheat the oven to 190°C (375°F, gas mark 5). Sift the flour, cocoa and baking powder together in a bowl.
2. Mix the sugar and melted margarine and add the water. Fold in the dry ingredients and pour into two greased and lined tins.
3. Bake for about 25 minutes, or until a cocktail stick inserted in the centre comes out clean. Cool on a wire tray and decorate.

You will need for the optional filling and topping (halve the quantity for filling only):
>   125 g (4 oz) margarine
>   170 g (6 oz) icing sugar
>   Flavouring of choice, e.g. 25 g (1 oz) cocoa, mixed with
>   1 tablespoon very hot water or 1 tablespoon instant
>   coffee and some nuts

CHOCOLATE MALT CAKE

You will need:

175 g (6 oz) wholemeal flour

2 teaspoons baking powder

25 g (1 oz) cocoa

175 g (6 oz) molasses or brown sugar

2 eggs, beaten

120 ml (4 fluid oz) oil

120 ml (4 fluid oz) milk

2 tablespoons malt extract

For the topping:

125 g (4 oz) low fat cream cheese

75 g (3 oz) plain chocolate

Method:

1. Preheat the oven to 170°C (325°F, gas mark 3) and grease and line two sandwich tins, 18 to 20 cm (7 to 8 inch).
2. Put the sugar, oil, eggs, milk and malt extract into a large bowl and mix well.
3. Add the flour and sift in the cocoa and baking powder. Beat until smooth.
4. Divide between the sandwich tins and smooth flat.
5. Bake for 25 to 30 minutes, until springy.
6. Turn out and cool on a wire rack.
7. Melt the chocolate over a bowl of hot water or in a microwave. Beat the cream cheese until smooth and add the melted chocolate. Beat well.
8. Put half the filling between the two parts of the cake and spread the rest on the top. Make a pattern with a fork to finish.

CHOCOLATE FUDGE CAKE

We can't be health conscious all the time. Even people with diabetes are allowed a birthday cake (well, a small piece, anyway). This delicious recipe fits the bill perfectly.

You will need:

250 g (8 oz) plain flour

125 g (4 oz) soft brown sugar

125 g (4 oz) plain chocolate
125 g (4 oz) margarine
125 g (4 oz) caster sugar
2 eggs, separated
300 ml (½ pint) semi-skimmed milk
1 teaspoon bicarbonate of soda
For the chocolate fudge topping:
125 g (4 oz) icing sugar
1 tablespoon milk
25 g (1 oz) margarine
1 tablespoon cocoa

Method:

1. Preheat the oven to 180°C (350°F, gas mark 4) and grease and line a 20 cm (8 inch) baking tin.
2. Put the chocolate, some of the milk and the brown sugar into a saucepan and melt slowly. Stir in the rest of the milk.
3. Whisk the margarine with the caster sugar until light and fluffy and then beat in the egg yolks, one at a time.
4. Sift the flour and bicarbonate of soda together into the creamed ingredients and add the chocolate and milk. Beat until smooth.
5. Whisk the eggs whites until stiff and then fold carefully into the batter.
6. Bake for about 45 minutes, until springy.
7. Turn out and cool slightly on a wire rack while you make the icing.
8. Put the fat and the milk into a saucepan and heat gently until melted.
9. Sift in the icing sugar and cocoa and mix well. Spread over the cake while still slightly warm.

CHOCOLATE MUFFINS

Bicarbonate of soda has the effect of reddening cakes that have cocoa as an ingredient, giving rise to the name of Devil's food cake. These very chocolatey muffins are a deep, rich colour and flavour, and also low in sugar. I forgot to put any in the first time I made them, and they still tasted OK, but they were even better with a little sugar.

You will need:

240 g (8 oz) plain flour
80 g (3 oz) cocoa
60 g (2 oz) sugar
1 teaspoon bicarbonate of soda
Pinch of salt
160 ml (6 fluid oz) milk
40 ml (1½ fluid oz) vegetable oil
1 egg
120 g (4 oz) chocolate chips

Method:

1. Preheat the oven to 200°C (400°F, gas mark 6).
2. Sift the flour, salt, cocoa and bicarbonate together and add the sugar.
3. Mix together the egg, milk and oil in a separate bowl.
4. Spoon the two mixtures together, with half of the chocolate chips. Keep mixing to the minimum.
5. Spoon into paper cases and sprinkle the rest of the chocolate chips on the tops.
6. Bake for about 20 minutes.

FLORENTINES

You will need:

50 g (2 oz) butter
50 g (2 oz) caster sugar
50 g (2 oz) chopped almonds
1 tablespoon flour
1 tablespoon sultanas
1 tablespoon chopped candied peel
1 tablespoon cream
80 g (3 oz) dark chocolate
3 glacé cherries, chopped

Method:

1. Grease and flour two baking trays and preheat the oven to 180°C (350°F, gas mark 4).
2. Melt the butter in a pan, add the sugar and bring to the boil for 1 minute. Remove from the heat.
3. Blend in all the other ingredients except the chocolate.
4. Put teaspoons of the mixture onto the baking trays

with plenty of room to spread.

5. Bake for 10 minutes and leave to cool on the tray for 5 minutes.

6. Heat the chocolate in a bowl over hot water. Spread a little of the melted chocolate over the base of each biscuit with a fork and allow to cool before serving.

CHOCOLATE CHIP OATMEAL COOKIES

No chocolate book would be complete without such a recipe, but I thought I'd include some with oats, which are really good for you.

You will need: **Makes 12**

    30 g (1 oz) butter
    80 g (3 oz) brown sugar
    1 tablespoon milk
    80 g (3 oz) flour
    ¼ teaspoon bicarbonate of soda
    Pinch of salt
    100 g (4 oz) rolled oats
    100 g (4 oz) chocolate chips
    50 g (2 oz) chopped nuts (optional)

Method:

1. Preheat the oven to 190°C (375°F, gas mark 5).

2. Beat the butter and sugar together until creamy. Add the milk and beat well.

3. Fold in the sifted flour, bicarbonate of soda and salt. Stir in the oats, chocolate chips and nuts, if using any.

4. Drop tablespoonfuls onto ungreased baking sheets. Bake for 9 to 10 minutes for chewy biscuits or 12 to 14 minutes for crispy ones. Cool for a minute or so on the baking sheet and then remove them to a wire rack.

BRAZILIAN BROWNIES (PEDACINHOS)

These brownies are delicious served with Hot Mocha Chocolate.

You will need:
- 2 tablespoons melted butter
- 4 tablespoons flour
- 1 tablespoon water
- 4 tablespoons sugar
- 1 teaspoon baking powder
- 3 eggs
- 3 tablespoons cocoa powder

Method:

1. Prepare a 20 cm (8 inch) baking tin and preheat the oven to 180°C (350°F, gas mark 4).

2. Mix the butter and sugar together until creamy.

3. Add the eggs and then the sifted flour, baking powder and cocoa. Mix well and add the water, if required.

4. Bake for about 25 minutes, or until done. Cool in the tin before cutting into squares.

CHOCOLATE PETIT FOURS

You will need: **Makes about 20**
- Sweet paper cases
- 250 g (8 oz) dark chocolate
- 4 tablespoons water
- 1 tablespoon strong coffee
- 50 g (2 oz) butter
- 2 egg yolks
- 1 teaspoon rum or other liqueur (optional)

Method:

1. Break half the chocolate in a bowl over a pan of hot water. When melted, line each sweet paper case with a teaspoon of chocolate spread round the base. Leave to set.

2. Break the remaining chocolate and put into a saucepan with the coffee and water. When melted, bring to the boil, stirring. Remove to cool.

3. Beat in the butter and the egg yolks and rum. Leave until cold.

4. If you are feeling brave, remove the chocolate cases from their paper, but if not, leave them in and tip each one with the chocolate cream and leave to set. Refrigerate and eat fairly soon.